Now

by

on the movie screen

starring

KEIR DULLEA · SUSAN PENHALIGON

Leopard in the Snow

Guest Stars

KENNETH MORE · BILLIE WHITELAW

featuring GORDON THOMSON as MICHAEL
and JEREMY KEMP as BOLT

Produced by JOHN QUESTED and CHRIS HARROP
Screenplay by ANNE MATHER and JILL HYEM
Directed by GERRY O'HARA

An Anglo-Canadian Co-Production

ANNE MATHER

a trial marriage

Harlequin Books

TORONTO • LONDON • NEW YORK • AMSTERDAM • SYDNEY

CHAPTER ONE

Jake Courtenay stood at the long windows of his first
floor suite in the Tor Court Hotel, staring out broodingly
over the harbour. In the height of summer, the quay was a
hive of activity, with fishing smacks and pleasure boats and
sailing craft all vying for space in the crowded inner
harbour. But in November most of the sailing boats were
shrouded with tarpaulin, and although a few hardy yachts-
men braved the autumn gales, most of their owners had
packed up and gone away for the winter.

Jake's mouth turned down at the corners. Who could
blame them? Torquay in November was no seething Mecca
of entertainment, and certainly had the choice been left to
him, he would not have chosen this hotel. Of course, he
could have stayed at the Boscombe Court in Bournemouth,
or the Helford Court in Falmouth, or even the Fistral Court
in Newquay, but they were all pretty much the same at this
time of the year. His own choice veered more towards the
Parkway Court in New York, or the Boulevard Court in
Paris, and if he had to have sea air, then the Court Medi-
terranée in Cannes or the Court Italia in Juan les Pins was
more to his taste.

But the choice had not been his. The specialist's advice
had been more than eloquent. Indeed, his words had been
more in the nature of a dictate than an opinion. Complete
rest for at least six months—no work, no travel, no business meetings, no hectic social gatherings, no alcohol—no
stress.

Maxwell Francis was a friend, of course, as well as a very
successful consultant to the rich and famous. He was used
to high-powered business men, who lived on their nerves,
and fed their ulcers with champagne and caviare. He was
used to treating heart complaints and nervous disorders,
brought on by the pressure of living always one step ahead
of the rest.

5

his own brain. It was rather a case of the flesh being willing and the spirit being weak. That small, rather ugly mass of tissue inside his skull gave up the race and Jake found himself the victim of the disease he had so long despised.

He wondered when the pace of living had first begun to tell. When his marriage to Denise broke up, perhaps? And yet, even in those days, he had been working too hard. One of the reasons Denise had given for the irretrievable break-down of their relationship had been his obsession for work, although she had been more than willing to enjoy the fruits of his labours. But she liked the high life, and when his work took him away from the jet-flight capitals she pre-ferred, she had had few scruples about finding some other man to share her charms—and her bed.

Jake had been philosophical about her indiscretions. His own life was not so blameless at that time, and if Denise required that kind of stimulation, she could hardly object if he required the same. Until some obscure Italian prince came along and offered her his title as well as his fortune. The idea of being Princess Denise had appealed to her, and she had been able to overlook the fact that her Italian was at least forty years older than she was, and hardly able to stand the pace she set.

But that was Denise's problem. For Jake's part, he scarcely noticed her passing. Their association had drifted so far from any conventional marriage that he had mentally breathed a sigh of relief to be free again. It was a blessing they had had no children. But again, Denise had not wanted them, and although Jake had known his parents had been disappointed that he had not produced a son to follow in his footsteps, he himself knew how much a child of their marriage might have suffered. Nevertheless, after that, he had shared no lasting relationship with any woman. His work had filled his days—and his nights, as well.

And now he was here. A guest in one of his own hotels, identified to nobody except the hotel manager, Carl Yates, who was a personal acquaintance. This had been Maxwell's

futility, Jake seated himself beside the trolley and uninterestedly helped himself to a cucumber sandwich. His appetite was still persistently absent, and food was no more than a rather annoying necessity to living. Living! An ironic humour curled his thin lips. Was this living? Or just *existing*? And what was at the end of it? Would he ever retrieve that enthusiasm for his work which had motivated his life? Without it, he was only half a man.

He rose from his chair again and went back to the window, a tall, rather gaunt figure in the close-fitting dark pants that moulded his lean hips, and a tawny-brown sweater. Strands of silky-smooth dark hair overlapped his collar at the back, liberally streaked with grey. These past few months had laid their mark upon him, and he knew that no one would mistake his age at present as they had done in the past. There were lines etched beside his mouth and nose which had not been there before, and his eyes seemed sunken into his skull. Yet for all that, he was a man who would always attract women, and the hooded depths of dark eyes still proved an irresistible lure.

Along the parade, several shoppers struggled towards the bus ranks, and the light from shop windows spread out across the harbour. There were cars streaming towards the outskirts of the town and Paignton beyond, the curve of the headland a mass of winking lights. His own car languished in the hotel garage, only to be used on very rare occasions. Driving, like everything else he enjoyed, had become a strain.

The grounds fronting the hotel were not extensive. A low stone wall divided them from the promenade beyond, and within the circle the wall provided a few stout palms spread their leaves among less exotic specimens of greenery. Floodlights had been installed among the shrubs so that in summer the Tor Court could hold its own with the other hotels that flaunted themselves after dark in a welter of coloured lights. But during the winter they went unused—except at Christmas.

Looking down, Jake had a first-rate view of the entrance,

doing a worthwhile job of work? It was nothing to do with him. Besides, judging by the amount of jewellery Mrs Faulkner-Stewart wore, and the expensiveness of her furs, she could obviously afford the best of everything, and probably the girl took her for every penny she could make. The only inconsistent factor was why she had chosen to winter at the Tor Court instead of in Cannes or Madeira, or any one of a dozen other fashionable locations.

By the time he had finished his tea it was dark outside, and on impulse, he decided to go for a walk. At least that was one pastime which had not been denied to him, but he obediently put on his thick, fur-lined duffel coat before leaving the room. The cold was something else he had to guard against, although he refused to put on the marathon-length woollen muffler his mother had crocheted for him.

The lift took him down to the lobby where Carl was standing, talking to his receptionist. The manager lifted his hand in greeting, but Jake had no desire to get involved in conversation with him and with a brief acknowledgement, strode towards the revolving doors. His hand had reached out to propel them forward when he became aware of the girl who had been occupying his thoughts earlier approaching over the soft grey carpet, pulled along by the enthusiastic efforts of her employer's black poodle.

He paused, and the second's hesitation was enough to create a situation where it would have been rude of him to barge ahead without acknowledging her presence. He guessed she would use the baggage door to let the dog out, and with a feeling of compulsion, propelled it open and waited for her to pass through.

Anticipating his intention, she had quickened her step, and her shoulder brushed the toggles of his coat as she said a breathy: 'Thanks!' passing him to emerge into the cool, slightly frosty air. In a waist-length leather jerkin and dusty pink flared pants she seemed hopelessly underdressed for the weather, but Jake inwardly chided himself for his concern. She was young—and *healthy*; an enviable condition!

11

was his middle name—James Allan Courtenay—and it had seemed a good idea to use that and avoid possible recognition. But it still gave him a moment's pause. He wondered how she knew his name, and decided he would have a few harsh words to say to Carl Yates the next time he saw him.

Now he merely nodded, pressing his hands more deeply down into the pockets of his duffel coat, and she supplied the answer to his unspoken question without even being aware of doing so.

'Della—Mrs Faulkner-Stewart, that is—asked the receptionist who you were,' she exclaimed casually. 'Della always likes to know the names of the other guests. I hope you don't mind.'

Jake glanced at her then, and the humorous mobility of her wide mouth inspired the distinct impression that she knew very well that he did mind. But he refused to justify her amusement by admitting the fact.

'It's no secret,' he said abruptly, and she shrugged, tucking her cold hands into the slip pockets of her jerkin. The wind was tugging at her hair, however, and every now and then she had to lift a hand and push it back from her eyes and mouth. Strands blew against the sleeve of his coat, and their brightness irritated him.

For a few minutes they walked in silence, and then she spoke again: 'My name's Rachel—Rachel Lesley. I work for Mrs Faulkner-Stewart.'

Jake drew a deep breath, but made no comment, and all at once he was aware of a stiffening in her. Perhaps she was getting the message at last, he thought ruthlessly, and was totally unprepared for her attack when it came.

'You're not very polite, are you?' she inquired, with cool audacity. 'Why don't you just tell me to get lost, if that's the way you feel?'

Her words stopped Jake in his tracks, and he turned to stare at her angrily. 'I beg your pardon?'

'You heard what I said,' she insisted, and he saw that the eyes turned belligerently up to his were flecked with

girl exclaimed: 'Oh, glory!' and darted forward to rescue the poodle's collar, and her laughing apology to the red-faced woman in charge of the Pekinese brought an unwilling deprecation from her lips. Jake watched the exchange with reluctant admiration, and then realised he was wasting a perfectly good opportunity to make his departure. Curiously enough he was less eager to leave now, but the remembrance of what the girl had said still rankled, and ridiculous though it was he resented the feeling of being the object of anyone's pity. That was something he could do without.

Even so, he couldn't resist a glance over his shoulder as he walked away between the cultivated borders, and felt a moment's regret when he saw she had turned back towards the hotel. But only a moment's. She was a nice kid, and probably he had judged her too harshly—after all, nowadays young people seemed to have few inhibitions about anything, and she had only been friendly, as she said—but it wasn't in his interests to become too friendly with anyone at the hotel. No matter how nice people were, they always wanted to know everything about you, and that was something Jake wanted to avoid. Besides, he could imagine Mrs Faulkner-Stewart's reactions if she thought her companion was becoming friendly with a man of his age. No matter how innocent an association might be, someone could always put the wrong interpretation upon it. He could almost see the headlines in the newspapers now: *Middle-aged tycoon takes rest cure with schoolgirl!* God, he shuddered to think of it. The poodle had provided him with a lucky escape, and in future he would ensure that his walks did not coincide with exercising the dog.

couple of insurance policies, which would provide sufficient funds to pay all outstanding debts, she was penniless, had left her curiously unmoved.

That was when Della Faulkner-Stewart had taken over. She had been a school friend of Rachel's mother's, and although they had not seen her for some years, she had arrived in Nottingham for Mr Lesley's funeral. That she was still in town when Mrs Lesley also died was, she said, a blessing, and she had insisted that Rachel should not attempt her final examinations at such a time. There was no hurry, she said. She herself needed a companion—her previous companion had taken the unforgivable step of getting married—and why didn't Rachel come and live with her for a while? They could help one another.

In her numbed state, Rachel was only too willing to let someone else take responsibility for her. It wasn't until some weeks afterwards, when she found herself at Della's constant beck and call, that she began to appreciate what she had forfeited. But still, she had a little money of her own, and until she could afford to take her finals, she was persuaded that she could be a lot worse off.

Della's husband was dead, too, and sometimes Rachel wondered whether that was why she had come to Nottingham in the first place. Perhaps she had hoped to persuade Rachel's mother to take over the position as her companion, but Mrs Lesley had been too grief-stricken at that time to consider it. The truth was, Della was not the most considerate of employers, and although her husband had left her comfortably placed, she resented being without a man to care for her. Consequently, she spent little time at her London home, preferring to live in hotels, always in the hope of finding some man to take her late husband's place. Her only stipulation was that he should be English. She despised Europeans, and seldom went abroad, preferring wholesome British food to what she termed as 'foreign muck'.

Yet, for all that, Rachel was not actively unhappy. On the contrary, she was naturally a pleasant-natured girl, and

ance, he aroused the most wanton thoughts inside her. His attraction for her owed little to whatever illness had brought him here, and she knew that Della would have a fit if she guessed the fantasies Rachel was nurturing. But they were only fantasies, she told herself severely, dragging Minstrel into the lift after her, and showing an unusual lack of sympathy when she accidently stepped on his paw.

Della's suite of rooms was on the second floor. She had reserved a lounge and a double room with bath for herself, as well as a single room for Rachel. Rachel was obliged to use the bathroom on that floor which served two other rooms as well as her own, but she didn't mind. She invariably took her bath in the evening, while everyone else was in the bar enjoying pre-dinner drinks, and unlike Della she had felt little desire to mix with her fellow guests—until now.

When she and Minstrel entered the suite, Della called peevishly from the bedroom: 'Rachel, is that you?' And when the girl showed her face at the bedroom door: 'You've been a long time.'

Della had had one of her headaches when Rachel went out. They were a persistent torment to her, she declared, although they came in very useful on occasion, when she wanted rid of Rachel for the afternoon.

Now, however, she levered herself up on the quilted counterpane, looking suitably wan in her lacy pink negligée. She was forty-three, and spent half her life trying to look younger, with the inevitable result of achieving the opposite. Her fine hair had been tinted so often that it looked like dried straw until it had been combed into its usual style, and her skin was paper-thin and veined from too much food and too little exercise. She treated Rachel with a mixture of envy and irritation, and disliked feeling at a disadvantage with anybody.

Now Rachel held on desperately to Minstrel's lead, as he viewed the tempting expanse of soft cream carpet spread out before him, and explained: 'I couldn't find that particular brand of cream anywhere. I think Mr Holland must make it up for you.'

she thought irritably. But she had never been troubled with such ideas before.

The usual arrangement was that Della went down to the cocktail bar before dinner and shared in the casual conversation of her fellow guests, while Rachel tidied the suite, fed Minstrel, and had her bath. Then, later, they would meet up again in the restaurant and share a table for dinner. After dinner, a few of the guests made up a four for bridge, and as Della enjoyed cards she was invariably included. That was Rachel's cue to do as she liked, but this usually comprised a walk with Minstrel, followed by television and bed, in that order. Occasionally she had agreed to a date with a member of the hotel staff; but these were few and far between, preferring as she did the comparative luxury of reading in her own room, briefly free of Della's fads and fancies.

This evening, however, Rachel felt restless, and after spending longer over her toilette than she normally did, she was late for dinner. She had hesitated a long while over what she should wear. After discarding the chemise dress she had planned to wear in favour of velvet pants and an embroidered smock, she had eventually returned to her original choice, deciding she was being silly in imagining it mattered either way. The chemise was long and made of white sprigged cotton, a ribbon tie beneath her breasts accentuating their fullness; but it was definitely not the sort of dress an older woman would wear, and that was why Rachel had hesitated over wearing it. But she was not an older woman, and there was no use wishing she was.

The lift seemed grindingly slow as it descended to the lower floors, and Rachel was biting her lips impatiently when it stopped at the first landing. Then she stepped back nervously, her cheeks darkening with hot colour when she saw the man waiting to get into the lift. His own expression was less easy to define, but after only a moment's hesitation he stepped inside, joining her in the suddenly overpoweringly confined atmosphere of the square cubicle. In a navy suede suit and a matching shirt, the heavy duffel coat overall, he reduced the proportions of the lift alarm-

she had to go and face Della's undoubted irritation because she was late.

But as she crossed the lobby towards the restaurant, Carl Yates' voice hailed her. The young manager of the Tor Court would stir a few hearts himself, she thought inconsequently, although she herself didn't go for husky Vikings with shoulder-length blond hair.

'Oh, Miss Lesley,' he said now, his roving eyes revealing a deepening interest. 'Mrs Faulkner-Stewart asked me to get her tickets for the concert at the Conservatory.' He waved a white envelope. 'Will you give them to her?'

'Thank you.'

Rachel took the envelope, wondering why he had chosen to give her the tickets. Normally he used bell-hops to run his messages for him, and he must know that Della was always to be found taking dinner at this time.

'You're looking particularly attractive this evening, Miss Lesley,' he continued, with the assurance of a man not accustomed to being rebuffed. 'I didn't know you knew Jake—Allan.'

Rachel's smile was forced. 'I'll give Mrs. Faulkner-Stewart the tickets,' she said, and gained a certain malicious satisfaction from his chagrin as she sauntered into the restaurant.

Della had not waited for her. She was already half-way through her smoked salmon, and she took the envelope Rachel proffered with unconcealed annoyance.

'I don't pay you to loiter about in hotel lobbies, Rachel!' she stated, in audible tones, and Rachel couldn't help reflecting, as she reached for an olive, that pride always came before a fall.

Even so, as she lay in bed that night, she found herself reliving those moments in the lift. So—his name was Jake. At least she could thank Carl Yates for that small piece of information. Jake Allan? Yes, she liked it. It suited him.

During the following days, Rachel had little time to herself. Della took to her bed with a stomach disorder the morning following the encounter in the lift, and her fretful demands kept her companion on her toes. There was not

'What about?' Della looked suspicious.

'Nothing much.' Rachel managed to distract her attention by opening the menu. 'Oh, look! They've got your favourite food here. Tournedos! They must have known you'd be feeling better this evening.'

When the meal was over, the elderly Colonel Della had been grumbling about earlier approached their table. He subjected Rachel's cleavage to minute inspection, and then turning to Della exclaimed gallantly: 'Good to see you back, my dear. Game hasn't been the same without you! You will be joining us this evening, I hope.'

Della's indignation melted beneath such outright flattery.

'I've missed our little get-togethers, too, Colonel,' she assured him coyly. 'And I know it's no fun playing with three and a dummy hand.'

The Colonel's wicked old eyes flickered over Rachel again. Then he turned his attention to what Della was saying: 'What? Oh, yes. Well, as a matter of fact, dear lady, we managed to persuade one of the other guests to join us yesterday evening. You've probably seen him around. A Mr Allan.'

Rachel managed to control the start the Colonel's words had given her, and concentrated on her hands curled tightly together in her lap, as Della answered: 'Mr *Allan*!' Her interest was evident. 'Oh, yes. I know who you mean, Colonel. But . . .' She paused, obviously searching for words to disguise her real feelings. 'He seems such a—quiet man. Always keeping himself to himself.'

'Yes.' The Colonel was losing interest in the conversation. 'So you'll be joining us later?'

'Of course.' Della moistened her upper lip. 'Will—er—will Mr Allan be joining us this evening?'

The Colonel shook his head, and unable to catch Rachel's attention, started to move away. 'Shouldn't think so. Only played because I bullied him into it. See you later, dear lady.'

After the Colonel had gone, Della made a little sound of

25

Rachel would have gone past him, but he spoke again: 'Can I buy you a drink?'

She halted, and turned to look at him. 'No, thanks.'

'Why not?'

She hesitated, tempted to brush him off without a second thought, but out of the corner of her eye she suddenly saw that Jake Allan had just entered the hotel and was crossing the lobby towards them. If she walked away now, he would no doubt stop to speak to the manager, and she would have no opportunity of speaking to him herself.

'I—er—I don't drink,' she averred, mentally measuring the narrowing distance between herself and Jake Allan.

'I'll buy you a tomato, juice, then,' suggested Carl eagerly, but before she could reply a shadow fell across them. Carl turned half impatiently, to see who dared to interrupt them, but quickly schooled his features when he recognised the man. Rachel was impressed. Whoever Jake Allan was, he certainly had the power to bring Carl to attention.

'Good evening,' he said, his dark gaze flickering over Rachel with ruthless detachment. 'Good evening, Carl.'

Carl nodded and smiled, shifting rather awkwardly. 'Did you enjoy your walk, Mr Allan?'

Mr Allan! Rachel raised her dark eyebrows. What had happened to the casual use of the man's Christian name?

'Very much,' Jake Allan was saying now, with a slight upward lift of his mouth. 'Is dinner over?'

Carl nodded. 'Oh, yes. Some minutes ago. Er—the game's begun.'

'Good.' Jake's dark eyes shifted to Rachel again. 'How are you, Miss Lesley? I haven't seen you about the hotel for some days.'

Rachel's knees resumed their unsteady wobbling. 'I— Mrs Faulkner-Stewart has been—indisposed. I've been taking care of her.'

'Very well, I'm sure,' he conceded with faint mockery. He flicked an assessing look in Carl's direction, as if summing up the situation. 'Now, if you'll excuse me . . .'

Rachel cast a dismayed look at Carl, and then, stumbling

27

'Wh—what alternative?'

He sighed, as if becoming impatient with himself as well as her. 'What's your name? Rachel? Rachel—do you know how old I am?'

She shrugged uncertainly. 'Thirty-eight, thirty-nine . . .'

'I'm forty-one. How about you?'

She shifted from one foot to the other. 'Nearly nineteen.'

'Eighteen!'

'All right. Eighteen.'

He raised his eyes heavenward. 'I must be out of my mind!'

Without another word he stepped out of the lift, and the automatic mechanism set the doors gliding closed. Unable to prevent herself, Rachel pressed the button to open the doors again, and stepped through them, feeling a sense of inevitability as they closed behind her, and the lift whined away upward.

Jake, who had been striding along the corridor towards his apartments, glanced over his shoulder as he heard the lift depart, and his brow furrowed angrily when he saw Rachel standing there. He halted abruptly and came slowly back to her, his hands deep in the pockets of his coat.

'What do you think you're doing?' he demanded.

Rachel shook her head, unable to voice what she had thought. 'I—I can use the service stairs,' she stammered, and he uttered a word she scarcely understood.

'You'd better go,' he said. 'If anyone sees you on this floor——'

He broke off expressively, and her lips trembled. 'That would never do, would it?' she burst out, unable to prevent the words in her humiliation.

Jake's dark eyes raked her savagely. 'All right, all right,' he snapped. 'If you don't care, why should I?' He spread a mocking hand towards his door. 'Come into my parlour!'

Rachel pressed her lips together. 'Couldn't we—couldn't we have a drink together?'

'I thought I heard you telling Yates you didn't drink?' he countered.

CHAPTER THREE

AT least her surroundings were reassuring. This had to be the best suite in the hotel, she thought. Della's rooms were not like this, and the green and gold pattern of the carpet was reflected in the long curtains and matching cushions. A self-coloured hide suite looked soft, and squashily comfortable. There were several small tables, as well as a television, as big as the one downstairs, and the dining table, in the window embrasure, commanded a magnificent view over the lights of the harbour.

While she looked around, assuming an interest in the concealed lighting above the ceiling moulding, Jake took off his overcoat and slung it carelessly over a chair near the door. Then he moved to stand before the huge marble fireplace, obsolete now, since the introduction of central heating. Against its veined beauty his profile had a dark, forbidding quality, and a momentary sense of panic gripped her.

'Regretting it already?' he inquired dryly, and she looked up at him defensively.

'No.'

'Who were those women?'

'Acquaintances of Mrs Faulkner-Stewart,' replied Rachel offhandedly. 'You have a wonderful view——'

'Will they tell her where you are?'

Rachel sighed frustratedly. 'I don't know.'

'You're not worried?'

'No!'

He moved his shoulders in a gesture of dismissal, and her eyes were irresistibly drawn to the lean muscularity beneath the fine material. 'If you insist . . .' he commented carelessly. Then: 'Tell me about Mrs Faulkner-Stewart? Is she some relation of yours?'

'I've told you. She's my employer,' replied Rachel stiffly.

'Only that?' He seemed surprised. 'An unusual occupation for a girl of your age.' He paused. 'And generation.'

with surprising agility, interposing himself between her and the door, his fingers closing painfully round the soft flesh of her upper arm. She tried to pull away from him, alarmed by the smouldering look in his eyes, but he jerked her back against him, and she felt the hard length of his body against hers. His arms went round her, sliding across her flat stomach, propelling her closer, so that for the first time in her life Rachel could feel the throbbing heat of his desire.

'You have no conception of how I feel,' he protested roughly, bending his head to brush her neck with his tongue.

Rachel's panic began to subside. 'I—I thought you were angry with me,' she stammered.

'I am,' he retorted unsteadily. 'I shouldn't be holding you like this, and you shouldn't be letting me.'

'Why not?' Her mouth was dry, and she moistened her lips as his hands slid up over her rib-cage to cup her breasts.

But she knew. She had read books, and her instincts warned her that she was playing with fire. Yet she couldn't help herself. She wanted him to hold her, and the thin material of her chemise was no barrier to the way her breasts responded to his touch, swelling and hardening beneath his experienced fingers.

'Oh, Jake . . .' she breathed chokingly, using his name without thinking, and with a muffled oath, he twisted her round in his arms and covered her mouth with his.

A thousand stars seemed to explode in her head at the touch of his lips, and she clung to him desperately as the room swung giddily about her. She realised with a pang that she had never been kissed before this moment. The boyish embraces she had endured had never felt like this, and the muscled hardness of his thighs made her overwhelmingly aware of what she was inviting.

He released her lips to bury his face in her neck, his hands tangled in her hair, and she realised he was trembling. There was a heady intoxication in the knowledge

He was breathing hard. 'Well,' he ground out harshly, 'not to my knowledge. But I'm not such a swine as to take advantage of a girl young enough to be my daughter!'

Rachel caught her lip between her teeth. 'That's what you say . . .'

He made a bitter sound, dragging the palms of his hands down over his thighs. 'If you must know, I had a breakdown! I went to pieces. Couldn't work—couldn't sleep!' His lips curled. 'I was a wreck. But not impotent!'

Rachel pressed her palms to her hot cheeks. 'I—I suppose what you're really saying is, I—I'm not very good at it, am I?'

Jake stared at her frustratedly, and the intensity of his stare achieved its usual breath-stopping effect. Then he said flatly: 'All right—no. You're not very good. You're much too inexperienced.'

The callousness of his statement robbed her of what little composure she had left. 'Then—then why pretend it's anything else?' she cried tearfully, and appalled at her lack of self-control, she turned towards the door.

'Rachel!' His tone stopped her, containing as it did a reluctant reassurance. 'Rachel, I am sorry, believe me. But I am too old for you.'

She swung round again, searching his features for some sign of his real feelings. 'You're not old,' she exclaimed.

'I think we both know I am,' he said evenly. 'And what is more, if your employer learns that you've been here, I run the risk of being blacklisted by the management.'

Rachel bent her head, her hair tumbling with unknowing sensuality about her shoulders. 'I don't believe you care what the management think,' she retorted.

He sighed. 'Well, accept that I care what happens to you,' he said.

Her eyes lifted, seeking his. 'Do you?'

'Enough not to want to ruin your life,' he responded crushingly. 'But thank you for the compliment.'

'What compliment?'

He gave her a crooked smile. 'It's good for my morale to

didn't realise it was so late. I—I suppose I must have fallen asleep.' She coloured at the deliberate lie. 'I—I was watching television.'

'Huh!' Fortunately Della was too annoyed to notice the momentary hesitation. 'Well, I don't think it's too much to ask that you remember a dog needs exercising!' she declared. 'You're not exactly worked to death, are you?'

'No. I'm sorry.' Rachel really was, not least because the last thing she wanted now was a row with Della. 'It won't happen again.'

'See that it doesn't!'

Without even saying goodnight, Della marched away, every generous curve of her over-indulged body quivering with indignation.

Rachel closed the door again and breathed a deep sigh. She knew Della well enough to know that she had not heard the last of the matter. Her carelessness and lack of gratitude would be brought up on every occasion until her employer was satisfied that she was dutifully repentant.

Rachel didn't sleep well, which was hardly surprising in the circumstances. Her over-stimulated body would not let her rest, and Della's angry remarks had not in any way relieved her. Then a warm wind sprang up towards dawn which made the presence of the heating system almost unbearable.

At eight o'clock, she was up and dressed, and letting herself into Della's suite she retrieved the excitable poodle for an early outing. Minstrel showed his gratitude by smothering her in wet doggy kisses, the abrasive lick of his tongue a balm to her troubled spirit.

The sea-front was almost deserted and as the tide was out, she went down on to the damp sand, letting Minstrel off his leash to chase madly after gulls and sandpipers searching among the debris of seaweed on the shoreline. The wind was mild, blowing as it did from the south-west, and she breathed deeply, feeling its riotous fingers through her hair.

Back at the hotel, Della was preparing to go down for

'What's the matter with you this morning?' she inquired, pouring herself more coffee. 'Just because I had to chastise you about Minstrel, there's no reason to get huffy.'

'I'm not—huffy' Rachel reached for her own coffee cup, and then almost choked on its contents when the two women she and Jake had encountered on his landing the night before entered the dining room and approached their table.

Della watched her with evident impatience, and then smiled disarmingly as the two women stopped beside her. 'Good morning' she said, and indicated Rachel's discomfort with a casual wave of her hand. 'These young people! They're always in such a hurry.'

They both regarded Rachel without sympathy, and she wished she could dissolve into the floorboards at their feet. Then one of them said:

'Did you have a good game last evening, Della? I heard that you and Colonel Jameson made quite a killing.'

Della flushed with pleasure. 'Well—not exactly,' she demurred modestly 'But we did do rather well.'

'Yes.' The other woman's eyes flickered over Rachel, recovered now and watching the interchange warily. 'What a pity your companion doesn't play cards. We might make up another table with Mr Allan.'

Rachel's hands clenched together in her lap as Della said: 'I didn't know he played until the Colonel mentioned it. But he seems to keep very much to himself, doesn't he?'

The two women exchanged a glance and Rachel waited for the explosion their revelations would ignite. But instead of exposing her, they agreed with Della, and then excused themselves to move to their own table.

Rachel breathed a silent sigh of relief, but Della's next words were hardly reassuring:

'I'm thinking of giving a small dinner party tomorrow evening, Rachel Just myself and the Colonel, and one or two others. I wonder if Mr Allan would care to join us?'

The rest of the morning passed in a rather one-sided

as it was foolish. His fingers gripping her arm were painful, but she revelled in the sensation.

'Rachel!' When she made no immediate effort to answer him, he spoke again, glancing impatiently round the lobby, aware that no encounter in such public surroundings went unnoticed. 'Rachel, where have you been?'

'Walking.' She tried to pull herself together. 'I—how are you? It's a cold afternoon, isn't it? My hands are froz——'

'Rachel!' He said her name again as if he couldn't bear this time-wasting small talk between them. 'God, we can't talk here! Come with me! We'll walk along the front.'

But now Rachel found the strength to pull herself away from him, and moving her shoulders in a careless gesture, she said: 'I'm sorry, Mr Allan, I can't stop now. Della will be wondering where I am. I'll see you some other time, I expect——'

'Rachel!'

The smouldering darkness of his eyes had its usual effect on her knees, but she forced herself to move away from him, keeping a polite smile glued to her lips. She must not make a fool of herself now, not *here*, and she was very much afraid she might if he said anything more.

The distance to the lift stretched before her like the Gobi desert, but at last she was within the enclosing portals of the small cubicle which would lift her to the comparative safety of her own room. The last thing she saw as the doors closed was Jake standing where she had left him, staring after her, a curiously vulnerable expression on his lean features, and the tears overspilled her eyes.

Fortunately Della was downstairs, taking tea, and only Minstrel was there to share her misery. He was remarkably understanding for once, sensing her unhappiness and nuzzling against her comfortingly.

She managed to make some excuse to Della not to join her for dinner that evening, and had a sandwich brought up to her room. Exercising Minstrel was another matter, but although she looked about her nervously as she crossed the lobby with the poodle, there was no sign of the man who

Rachel tucked her trembling hands into the pockets of her jeans. She scarcely knew the Stranges, who were the second half of the bridge four. An elderly couple, they always seemed engrossed in their game, and paid little attention to anyone who didn't play. But the names of the two women who had seen her with Jake still had the power to send a shiver of apprehension down her spine. Nevertheless, it was Della's next words which caused her the most distress:

'And finally myself ... and Mr Allan! Yes,' this as Rachel's lips parted involuntarily, 'he's agreed to join us. Isn't that wonderful? I expect we'll have a bridge tournament later, now that we have eight players.'

Rachel turned away, pretending to search for Minstrel's lead, anything to conceal her tormented expression from Della's probing gaze. How could he, she thought despairingly, *how could he*? And why now? When in the past he had avoided contact with anyone?

'Well?' Della expected some response. 'Haven't you anything to say? Like—congratulations, for example?'

'Congratulations?' Rachel echoed blankly, schooling her features. 'I'm afraid I——'

'You know what a recluse Mr Allan has been,' exclaimed Della irritably. 'Don't you think it's significant that he's agreed to join *my* dinner party?'

'Oh, I see.' Rachel strove for control. 'I—well, yes. You —you've been very fortunate.'

'That's what Miss Hardy said,' remarked Della, frowning. 'Although I wouldn't have put it exactly like that myself. After all, it's obvious he's a man of the world, well used to the society I can offer. It's natural that as two—sophisticates—in what is without question an unsophisticated gathering, we should have certain things in common.'

Rachel grasped Minstrel's lead like a lifeline. 'You—you could be right,' she managed tightly. 'I gather you won't be—needing me this evening.'

'No. No.' Della could afford to be expansive. 'You go ahead and do whatever you want to do, my dear.' She

CHAPTER FOUR

DELLA dressed with extra care for her dinner party. Her gown of oyster pink chiffon floated about her plump figure with a flattering lack of definition, and the jewels that surrounded her neck, and hung with such vulgarity from her ears and fingers, denoted a richness seldom seen at the Tor Court. Her coiffure must be right, too, and Rachel's fingers were aching by the time she had twisted and coaxed Della's coarse hair into a becoming style.

'You really are getting rather good,' Della complimented her grudgingly when she had finished, turning her head this way and that to view the style from all angles.

Rachel put the brushes and combs away. 'Is that all?' she asked, and Della turned toward her curiously.

'What are you planning on doing this evening? Dining alone in the restaurant, or having something sent up here?'

Rachel shook her head. 'Neither. Actually, I've promised to have dinner with Mr—with Carl Yates,' she stated defiantly, waiting for the reproaches she was sure were to come, but for once Della was disposed to be generous.

'I'm glad,' she said, putting tissues into her evening purse. 'I don't like to think of you spending a lonely evening.'

Rachel thought, rather ungraciously perhaps, that Della had never before concerned herself with how many lonely evenings her companion spent, but obviously her success with Jake Allan had gone to her head. Now she was glad just to escape to her own room and take a hurried shower, refusing to admit, even to herself, that she regretted her defiant impulse to accept Carl's invitation.

She seldom wore pants in the evenings, but she wore them tonight. Black velvet pants, that teamed with a matching waistcoat, over a frilled white organdie blouse. The sleeves of the blouse were full, and she looked, she thought, like some medieval pageboy. Then she turned

round to half past ten. 'Della's arranged for one of the porters to let Minstrel out for a while, but she'll expect me to make sure he doesn't get into mischief.'

'Who?' inquired Carl wryly. 'The dog—or the porter?'

Rachel smiled. 'Minstrel, of course.'

'Don't you get sick of running after a woman like her?' he probed, but Rachel knew better than to discuss her employer with a man who was still practically a stranger to her.

'Della's been very good to me,' she told him quietly, and Carl was discreet enough to know that he was wasting his time making those kind of comments.

'Even so,' he persisted, 'you don't get a lot of free time, do you? I mean, it's a seven-days-a-week job really, isn't it?'

'I don't mind,' replied Rachel firmly, and he gave up asking questions.

In spite of her good intentions, it was after eleven-thirty before Rachel got back to the hotel. Some friends of Carl's arrived at the last minute, and they had insisted buying him a drink, although Rachel refused anything but fruit juice. She had had a couple of Martinis in the course of the evening, and she was determined not to add an aching head to her other problems.

She left Carl in the lobby, unutterably relieved when the night porter approached him with a message, thus preventing prolonged goodnights at her door. She thanked him politely for taking her, and because of the situation, Carl was obliged to let her go. But she realised she had been extremely fortunate in avoiding payment for his attentions.

Nevertheless, as the lift rode upward, all her other anxieties came back into focus, and she wondered whether she had been so clever, after all. What was the point of caring about a man who had made it blatantly obvious that to him she was nothing but a child?

As she came out of the lift, she wondered whether she ought to check on Minstrel, but then stifled the thought. It was late. No doubt Della would be in bed by now, and

'Della's party!' He repeated her words contemptuously. 'Damn you, you know I only agreed to join her band of card fanatics because I expected *you* to be there!'

'What?' Rachel stared at him disbelievingly. 'But I don't play cards——'

'How was I to know what your employer had planned? So far as I was concerned, it was a dinner party, nothing else. Naturally I expected you would be there.'

'Oh, Jake . . .' Rachel's knees gave out on her this time, and she sank down weakly on to the bed, staring up at him helplessly. 'Jake—I thought you'd done it deliberately.'

'Done what?' He came to stare down at her narrowly, his brooding gaze sending shivers down her spine.

'I—why, going to Della's party, of course. She said you had accepted her invitation, and I . . . I . . .'

Jake's eyes darkened. 'Is that why you went out with Yates?'

'Yes. Oh, yes!'

'I see.' He turned abruptly. 'That explains it.'

Rachel felt cold suddenly. 'Ex—explains it?' she echoed, as he walked deliberately towards the door. 'Is—is that all you came here for? To find out—why I went out with Carl Yates?'

Jake reached the door and turned, one hand on the handle. 'That's right. I had to know.'

Rachel got to her feet. 'But why?'

Jake bent his head. 'Call it what you like? Pride—curiosity.' He looked up. 'Or good old jealousy. It's all the same.'

'Jake!' She stared at him helplessly. 'Jake—please. Don't go!'

'I have to go,' he said roughly. 'I can't stay here all night.'

'You—you could,' she breathed huskily.

He shook his head slowly. 'No, Rachel. We both know I can't do that. Besides,' there was irony in his tone, 'I'm not allowed *any* kind of stimulation.'

'Oh, Jake!'

Before he could open the door, she flung herself across

Rachel's brow furrowed. 'I—I don't think I understand——'

'Rachel, the way I feel right now, I could handle anything, any situation! You give me strength—and confidence. You make me feel like a man again.'

'But that's good, isn't it?' she protested.

Jake inclined his head. 'Yes, it's good. Initially. But in the long term, it's—bad!'

'Why?'

Her eyes were wide and innocent, and he cursed himself for letting things get so out of hand. 'Rachel, you're eighteen! All right, I'll admit—I want you. I want to make love to you. I want to sleep with you. I want to wake up mornings and find your head beside mine on the pillow—but it won't do!'

She moved her head confusedly from side to side. 'Why won't it?'

With a stifled oath he released her, turning away to rake his fingers through his hair. 'Rachel, you know nothing about me, about my past, about my way of life.'

'I don't care about your past,' she exclaimed, shaking her head. 'This is what matters—here—and now!'

He swung round on her then, staring at her narrowly. 'Is that what you think? Is that what you really think? Are you so experienced in these matters that a night spent with me would mean nothing to you?'

Rachel's cheeks flamed. 'No! No, that's not what I mean, and you know it.'

'Then what are you saying?'

Rachel took a deep breath. 'I—I love you, Jake.'

His face changed, anger contorting his lean features. 'You don't love me, Rachel!' he told her ruthlessly. 'You only think you do. If you were honest, you'd admit you feel sorry for me. You see yourself as some kind of lady of charity, dispensing favours to the afflicted!'

'That's not true!'

'What is the truth, then?' he demanded. 'You want me to

'Why not?' She put up her hand to his cheek. 'Oh, Jake, I'll do anything you want me to do.'

'No!'

Again he let her go, moving away from her, running his hand round the back of his neck. Rachel watched him despairingly, not knowing what to say, how to appeal to him; only knowing that she loved him more than she had ever loved anyone in her whole life.

At last he turned and faced her, and she stiffened nervously at the serious look on his face. 'All right,' he said evenly, 'I'll lay it out for you, shall I?' He thrust his hands deep into the pockets of his velvet jacket. 'As I see it, it's like this; we could live together for a while—only I won't do that to you.' His lips twisted. 'Don't look like that, Rachel. You should be grateful——'

'Grateful!' she exclaimed bitterly. 'When you know how I feel . . .'

'Sure, sure.' He nodded heavily. 'Okay. There are other alternatives.'

'What?'

She was suspicious, and he gave a half smile. 'I'll be leaving here soon, but we could see each other again. Say, in six months from now——'

'Six months!'

Her cheeks lost their colour, and his teeth clenched impatiently. 'Rachel, it's the most sensible thing to do. We both need some time to get things into perspective.'

'Don't you mean out of it?' she demanded painfully. 'You know if you leave here, I'll never see you again!'

'That's not necessarily true,' he declared quietly. Then: 'There is one other way.'

'Why don't you suggest paying my way through college?' she cried chokingly. 'As you seem determined to treat me as a schoolgirl!'

'Is that what you want?' he asked grimly.

'No!' She stared at him tearfully. 'You know what I want.' She spread her hands. 'I want you . . .'

He took an involuntarily step towards her, and then

older than she was.' His lips curled, and she guessed what he was thinking 'Much like yourself,' he added ironically. 'Except that I'm no prince!'

'Jake!' Rachel refused to let him hold her off any longer, and she pushed aside his reluctant guard, reaching up to press her lips to his 'Oh, Jake, I'll marry you. On whatever terms you say you know that. But do you honestly think you'll be able to keep me away from you?'

His breathing quickened as her hands found the buttons of his shirt, tugging the expensive material aside to stroke the hair-roughened skin of his chest. There was an intense delight in being this intimate with him, and Jake was not immune to the probing caress of her fingers. He pulled her to him, not kissing her, just holding her closely, and her limbs melted against the hard strength of his body.

'Rachel!' With a groan, he put her away from him, cupping her face between his hands and looking down at her half impatiently. 'This has got to stop,' he insisted gently. 'And I must go. If we've got to face your formidable employer tomorrow, I think we should do it with a clear conscience, don't you?'

'You really mean it,' she breathed.

'Don't you?' For a moment his eyes clouded, but she quickly reassured him:

'Of course I do!' She bit her lower lip nervously. 'I—you won't let Della—I mean, if she gets angry, you won't—nothing will change your mind, will it?'

Jake ran a long finger over her parted lips. 'Only you can change my mind,' he told her softly, and she quivered when she considered the commitment she was making. She loved him, she didn't doubt that for a moment. But for a moment she wondered if that was enough . . .

Jake turned away and found the handle of her door. 'We'll have breakfast together,' he said. 'Can you manage that?'

'I—well, I usually have breakfast with Della . . .'

'All right.' He was unperturbed. 'I'll join you. How's that?'

understatement. Her face convulsed with colour and for an awful moment Rachel thought she was going to have a seizure. But then she went deathly pale, and sank down weakly on to the side of the bed, groping blindly for a tissue. Rachel watched her anxiously, twisting her hands together, and then sinking down on to her knees beside her, looking up into her distraught features.

'Are—are you all right?'

Della stared at her incredulously. 'Did I hear you correctly? You're going to—marry Allan?'

Rachel nodded her head. 'Yes.'

'But how—*when?* You don't know him!'

'I know him well enough,' said Rachel firmly. 'He—he asked me this evening.'

Della shook her head helplessly. 'But how could he? He was playing bridge until about—I don't know—an hour—an hour and a half ago!'

Rachel sought for words, the pain of her cheek a stinging reminder of Della's uncertain temper. 'We—we've known each other for about two weeks,' she ventured slowly. 'I—from the beginning, we were—attracted to one another.'

'But it's ridiculous!' Della was recovering rapidly; Rachel's passivity infuriated her. 'The man's at least twenty-five years older than you are!'

'Twenty-two, actually,' replied Rachel quietly.

'There you are, then! Twenty-two years, Rachel! He's more than old enough to be your father!'

'Age doesn't matter,' insisted Rachel, getting to her feet again. 'We love each other.'

But as she said the words, she wondered if that was strictly true. She had said she loved Jake, but he had only admitted that he *wanted* her! But he must love her, she told herself fiercely. You didn't marry someone unless you loved them.

Seeing the momentary uncertainty in the girl's face, Della too stood up. 'Love!' she said contemptuously. 'What is love but a satiation of the senses? How long do you think

Can you see yourself handling the kind of society he mixes in? My God, if it wasn't so tragic, I'd find it amusing!'

Rachel's face felt stiff and set. 'I don't care what you say, Della. I am going to marry him.'

'But you're too young, Rachel . . .'

'I'm growing older every minute.'

'So is he!' declared Della coldly, impatience returning. 'For heaven's sake, Rachel, think! It may seem a good idea now, but what happens in twenty years' time when you're my age and he's sixty!'

'I hope he'll still love me,' stated Rachel steadily, and Della uttered an ugly imprecation.

'You're a fool!' she exclaimed angrily. 'What do you really know about him, after all? A few clandestine meetings can't have told you a lot, except that he appears to prefer to keep you out of the limelight.'

'That's not true!' cried Rachel again, refusing to let her spoil what had been such a marvellous ending to her evening. 'We—we're having breakfast together tomorrow. He—he *was* going to speak to you then.'

'Really?' Della's lips curled. 'I suppose he told you he was going to ask my permission.'

'We don't need your permission,' repeated Rachel determinedly. 'Della, can't you at least say *one* thing in favour?'

'No.' Della was abrupt. 'I've told you what I think. God knows why he wants you, but he apparently does. You're attractive enough, I suppose, although he must meet dozens of women with more sex appeal than you have. You're young, of course. And hopelessly naïve. I suppose he thinks you'll be easy enough to get rid of when the time comes.'

'Please go, Della.'

Rachel had had enough. It was one thing to defend their discrepancies in age, and quite another to discuss the intimate side of their relationship. That was too private—too new—to bear exposure to Della's particular brand of malice.

'You'll regret this,' remarked Della, but she was moving

JAKE's car was a Lamborghini. After Della's revelations Rachel was hardly surprised, but its sleek green lines only served to emphasise the differences between them. Strapped into the safety harness, she viewed the passing countryside with a certain amount of trepidation, that owed nothing to the expert way Jake was handling the powerful machine.

But the day had not started well, and she could not pretend it had. She had slept very badly after the confrontation with Della, and awakened feeling totally incapable of facing the day ahead. Minstrel had still needed his walk, however, and until she actually left Della's employ, she felt obliged to exercise him.

Back at the hotel, Della had been waiting for her, and they went down to breakfast together, an almost unique experience. Rachel half wished she could have avoided this, but short of remaining in her room like the coward she felt herself to be, she was forced to go through with it. And after all, it was what she wanted, wasn't it? Only Della had planted the seeds of uncertainty inside her, and she had no one else to turn to for reassurance.

The dining room had not been busy. There was no sign of Jake, and for a few minutes she had wondered whether she had dreamed everything that had happened the night before. But five minutes later he had appeared, lean and attractive, in an expensively casual suede suit, his bronze roll-necked shirt both a complement and a contrast. Was it her imagination, Rachel wondered, or did he look different this morning, very much the assured and successful businessman he must have been before his illness; or was that only due to Della's influence? Whatever, she found it incredibly difficult to believe that a man of his experience and sophistication should find anything of interest in a nobody like herself, and when he stopped by their table she

choice in the matter, 'and I imagine we'll be married some time within the next two weeks.'

'Two weeks!' Now Della was really shocked. 'You can't mean that!'

In fact, Rachel herself was astounded by this news. *Two weeks!* Did he really intend to make her his wife in two weeks?

'I don't see any point in waiting, Mrs Faulkner-Stewart,' Jake continued implacably. 'Our minds are made up, and after Christmas I may not have the time to spare to give Rachel the attention she deserves. Besides,' he reached for Rachel's hand, and her heart skipped a beat as those hard brown fingers closed round hers, 'we don't want to wait, do we?'

Rachel shook her head, but her expression was hardly encouraging, compounding as it did a mixture of uneasy embarrassment and self-consciousness, and Della's lips thinned. 'Well, I think you're both behaving rather recklessly,' she declared coldly. 'You hardly know one another, and as I feel myself *in loco parentis*, as it were, so far as Rachel is concerned——'

'Rachel is eighteen,' Jake reminded her, equally coldly, and Rachel herself felt obliged to make a contribution:

'I'm going to marry Ja—Mr Courtenay,' she asserted, stiffly. 'I told you that last night, Della.'

After that, there was little more to be said. As soon as breakfast was over, Jake advised Rachel to go and get her coat, and this she did with alacrity, wishing above all things to avoid another confrontation with her employer. But when she came downstairs again Jake was alone in the lobby, and he explained briefly that Della was still in the dining room, probably relating the news to her cronies.

And now they were on their way to meet his parents. He had offered her no further explanations, just installed her in this luxurious vehicle, and made himself comfortable behind the wheel. A *fait accompli*, but Rachel felt as nervous as a teenager on her first date.

As if sensing the troubled train of her thoughts, he spoke at last, shifting his eyes briefly from the road to

He studied her troubled face expressionlessly. 'You've changed your mind,' he said flatly. 'I should have expected it.'

Rachel stared at him, her breast heaving with the tumult of her emotions. But she couldn't let him get away with that. 'I haven't changed *my* mind,' she declared tremulously, and he scowled.

'Are you suggesting *I* have?'

'I—why, no. Not exactly . . .'

'Then what are you saying?'

Her tongue appeared to wet her upper lip, its tentative exploration an unknowing provocation to the man watching her. With a muffled exclamation, he hauled her into his arms, and his mouth imprisoned the moistness she had just created.

'Oh, Rachel!' he breathed, one hand sliding possessively along the curve of her spine. 'Don't do this to me! I can't stand it.'

She was weak with longing for a satisfaction she had not received when he finally let her go, expelling his breath on a heavy sigh, resting his heated forehead against the coolness of the steering wheel. 'Well?' he said at last, turning his head sideways to look at her, and she allowed a faint smile to touch her lips.

'Della—Della made it all seem—impossible somehow,' she confessed, daringly running her own fingers over the muscular hardness of his thigh, and with a wry smile he lifted her hand and dropped it back into her lap.

'Della would,' he said, straightening his spine. 'Does her word mean that much to you?'

'Oh, no!' Rachel curled her legs up beneath her, and knelt there facing him. 'But—what she said, I felt—like a toy. Something amusing to be picked up for a while and then—dropped. Oh, she talked about you being too old for me, too, but that didn't matter. It was—it was you being—who you are.' She made a helpless movement of her shoulders. 'Are you really a millionaire?'

For a moment Jake's mouth hardened. 'Does it matter?'

'Do you want a drink before we meet my parents?' he asked, and she arched her eyebrows questioningly.

'I thought you weren't supposed to.'

'I said you, not me,' he corrected her, half mockingly. Then: 'No, Rachel, I don't need that kind of moral support. I know what I'm doing.'

'Do you?'

She stretched out her hand towards him and he took it in a firm grasp, his thumb probing the sensitive area of her palm. 'Oh, yes,' he insisted softly. 'I know.'

Rachel wished he would stop the car again and take her into his arms. Only there did she feel truly secure. Somehow, just looking at him, she could not believe this man really wanted her.

But he didn't, and needing some kind of contact, she said: 'Is it much further?'

Jake shook his head. 'About a mile, I guess. My father bought the old priory when he retired, and he's had it modernised for his own use.'

'The priory?' Rachel was intrigued. 'Was it really once a priory?'

Jake nodded. 'About two hundred years ago. Since then it's run through a variety of uses—almshouse, riding stables; once I believe it was used as a private school for the sons of gentlemen!'

Rachel looked ahead with enforced eagerness as they left the village behind and turned almost immediately on to a narrow private lane which led to the gates of the priory. But she was nervous, and she couldn't disguise the fact.

'You've seen my father before,' Jake remarked reassuringly, as they drove between iron gateposts and up a rhododendron-lined drive to the house. 'At the hotel. Remember?'

'So you did notice me,' she murmured with an attempt at lightness, and he gave her a lazy smile.

'I noticed,' he agreed dryly. 'Well, here we are!'

The priory still possessed a curious aura of asceticism. Maybe it was in the severe lines of the slate dark walls overhung with creeper, or simply that the cloistered

solid ground, Jake explained: 'This is my old nurse, Dora Pendlebury, Rachel. She and her daughter both live at the priory. Dora looks after the house-keeping and Sheila, that's her daughter, works as my father's secretary.' He paused. 'This is Rachel Lesley, Dora. My—fiancée.'

It was a unique experience, hearing herself described in those terms, and Rachel looked up at him before holding out her hand to the housekeeper. His eyes revealed that he was not unaware of the significance of his words and for a brief moment they shared an intimacy and was almost tangible. But when she turned back to Dora, Rachel surprised a curiously hostile reaction to their closeness, and a disturbing shiver of apprehension ran down her spine. They shook hands, and the housekeeper offered congratulations, but Rachel knew instinctively that Dora did not like her. She wondered why, and then dismissed the thought as Jake took her hand to guide her outside again.

'Are you warm enough? Do you need your coat?' he asked, as he closed the door behind them, but Rachel shook her head. The pants suit was warm, and the scarlet jersey she had teamed with it had a polo neck.

He led the way along a path that turned down the side of the building, and reached the stables by way of a kitchen garden where greenhouses bore witness to someone's horticultural ability. The stable yard was cobbled, and Jake briefly explained that this had once been the bakehouse.

'The ovens are still here,' he said, 'dating back to the eighteenth century, but they are used mostly for storing animal feed these days.'

Rachel knew his words were intended to reassure her, but she was tense as she accompanied him into a barn-like building, smelling of straw and disinfectant. If Dora had been disposed to dislike her without cause, what might she expect from his parents?

Three men and a woman were crowded around the stall where the foaling mare was lying, but the woman turned when she heard their footsteps, and exclaimed delightedly when she saw her son.

'Jake! Darling!' she cried, coming to meet him with out-

'Thank you,' and looked imploringly at Jake as if for inspiration. Taking pity on her, he said:

'I expect Rachel's frozen, aren't you? We didn't stop on our way here.'

'You didn't!' Mrs Courtenay clicked her tongue. 'Jake! You know what the doctors said about not overdoing things.'

'Leave him alone, Sarah.' Her husband shook his head in mock disapproval. 'He looks well enough to me.'

'He's too thin,' declared Mrs Courtenay at once. 'Much too thin. Jake, don't they feed you at the hotel?'

'I don't do anything to get hungry,' replied her son good-humouredly. 'How is our Lady?' He nodded towards the mare in the stall, and one of the other men present turned to speak to him.

'She's in a bit of a state, Jake,' he said, and Jake moved towards him, leaving Rachel with his parents.

'That's Sam Gordon,' Mr Courtenay told her. 'He looks after the horses for me, and that chap kneeling down beside the mare is Frank Evans, the local vet.'

Rachel cleared her throat. 'I—is the mare in trouble?' she got out nervously, and Mrs Courtenay sighed.

'She was too old to foal,' she stated impatiently. 'And now it's a breech.'

'She'll be all right,' said her husband doggedly. 'Frank won't let her down.'

To Rachel's surprise, Jake took off his jacket and hung it over the rail beside the vet's, squatting down on his heels beside the mare and running seemingly expert hands over its abdomen. They exchanged a few words on the mare's condition, and after a moment the vet nodded and got up to take a bottle of oil from his case.

'Jake!' His mother hastened to the rail to look down at him with evident concern. 'Come along. We'll go up to the house and have some coffee. Dora's preparing lunch for one, but there's plenty of time.' And when he ignored her, she added sharply: 'Don't go getting involved here, Jake. You're not fit.'

'If you say I'm not fit again, I'll——' Her son broke off

ceiling was arched and the original woodwork had been replaced with carved beams. The walls were also framed with wood, and hung with heavy apricot silk that was echoed in cushions and curtains, and the thick soft carpet underfoot. A grand piano stood at one end of the room, and its generous proportions in no way dwarfed a room which could happily accommodate a pair of sofas, at either side of the huge open fireplace. Yet, for all that, it was a lived-in kind of room, with well-stocked bookshelves and magazines strewn on a table near the hearth.

'Everything has to be on the grand scale here,' remarked Mr Courtenay, coming into the room behind Rachel and grinning wryly. 'Could you imagine this room with a conventional three-piece suite and little else? It would be lost.'

Rachel nodded. 'It's beautiful. A marvellous room for a party.'

'That's what we thought,' agreed Mr Courtenay, pulling a pipe out of his jacket pocket and putting it between his teeth. 'We may have the wedding reception here. What do you say?'

'Oh . . .' Rachel shifted awkwardly from one foot to the other. 'That's very kind of you.'

'Jake tells us your parents are dead,' inserted Mrs Courtenay. 'You're very young to be alone in the world.'

'Yes.' Rachel accepted Jake's father's invitation to sit on the edge of one of the tapestry-covered sofas, and looked up at her future in-laws nervously. 'My parents were only children, and I had no brothers or sisters.'

'You've been staying at the Tor Court, I believe,' went on Mrs Courtenay, ignoring her husband's silent admonition not to probe, and Rachel nodded.

'That's right. I've been working for a friend—a friend of my mother's, that is. I—she was visiting us when my mother died, and she suggested I needed to get away for a while.'

'Away from where?'

'Sarah!' Mr Courtenay sounded disgusted. 'Leave the girl

'I'm sure you do,' observed Mrs Courtenay thoughtfully, and Rachel wondered whether she had imagined a certain irony in her tone. Perhaps his mother thought she was marrying Jake for his money. Stranger things had happened, but until last night she had not known he had any money to speak of.

'I love Jake,' she said suddenly, surprising both his parents with her honesty. 'I'll do anything I can to make him happy.'

There were a few moments silence after her words, and then Mrs Courtenay said gently: 'Perhaps you will at that. You know of course that his previous marriage ended in the divorce court.'

'Yes.' Rachel's voice was steady.

'And you know he's been ill.'

'If she didn't already, she would now,' remarked Mr Courtenay, shaking his head. 'How you do harp on that subject, Sarah.'

'It's only right that Rachel should know all the facts, Charles,' declared his wife severely. 'Jake has been ill, and there's no point evading the issue.'

'Jake overworked!' retorted Mr Courtenay forcefully, and his wife seized on that point at once.

'Exactly,' she said. 'And yet you're still prepared to let him take over Sam's job in the stables the minute he gets home!'

'Of course.' Mr Courtenay was scathing. 'We both know that Jake would have preferred to work with animals, don't we? He enjoys it. But—to please me, and incidentally, you as well—he took over the Courtenay chain, and a damn fine job he's made of it.'

Rachel felt the need to make some contribution, if only to prevent their argument from escalating into something more serious: 'I didn't know Jake was interested in animals,' she said hastily.

Her words halted their interchange as she had hoped they would. 'He wanted to be a vet,' remarked his father, looking wryly at his wife. 'But he's our only son and natur-

with the disinfectant she had smelt earlier in the stables.

'I know,' he said, dropping down on to the couch beside her. 'I need a bath. I'll get one in a minute, but right now I could surely drink some coffee.'

His mother bustled with the cups, giving Rachel no chance to take charge, and he accepted the coffee from her with a lazily knowledgeable smile.

Rachel felt hopelessly inadequate. What had happened to her natural assurance, her ability to exchange small talk as she had done with the elderly regulars at the hotel? She had never been a particularly shy person, but suddenly she was allowing the overtones of the situation to colour her own personality. Money was not important, she told herself fiercely, but she wasn't convincing.

As if sensing her anxiety, Jake finished his coffee and rose to his feet, a hand on Rachel's wrist pulling her up, too. 'Do you mind if I show Rachel around, Mother?' he inquired, but it was purely a perfunctory question, for he was already crossing the room as he spoke, taking Rachel with him.

'Of course, go ahead.' His father acknowledged the gesture, but his mother had to have her say:

'Lunch is at one,' she warned. 'You've only got half an hour if you want to bathe and change.'

'All right, Mother.' Jake's tone was resigned. 'I'll have Rachel scrub my back if I don't have the time,' and ignoring his fiancée's burning cheeks, he hustled her out the door.

Once outside, however, his expression hardened slightly. 'This way,' he said, and releasing her arm, set off along the corridor leading into the west wing.

The room they entered was obviously his. Apart from the fact that it was excessively masculine in its austerity, wall photographs indicated his various stages of development, and cups occupying the top of a chest of drawers denoted the different sports he had competed in successfully.

Jake viewed the room without enthusiasm, however, and gesturing towards the cups exclaimed unsmilingly: 'My

terned bedspread, and stood regarding her grimly, hands pushed into his hip pockets as if to quell the urge to take hold of her.

'Rachel, I'm not trying to start an argument with you, but these people are only my parents. I want you to feel— at home with them, not on edge!'

Rachel held up her head. 'What you're really saying is if I can't get along with your parents, I haven't much chance of getting along with your friends, is that it?'

'No!' He spoke violently. 'That's not what I'm saying at all. I just want you to relax, that's all.'

'And what if I can't?'

He shook his head abruptly, turning away to grip the edge of the dressing table behind him, and anxiety over-rode all else. 'Jake!' She was beside him in a moment. 'Are you all right?'

The face he turned towards her was paler than before, and she realised what a strain this was for him, too. 'I guess Lady took more out of me than I thought,' he mut-tered, his mouth twisting with self-derision. 'Watch this space, Rachel! Be sure you know what you're getting into.'

'Oh, Jake!' She stared up at him appealingly, but he drew back from her obvious invitation.

'I'm sorry if I was brutal,' he said heavily. 'As you can see, even the smallest amount of exertion reduces me to this! Put it down to body fatigue. Obviously I'm not as fit as I thought I was.'

'Jake . . .' Rachel's nails dug into her palms. 'Do you honestly think that makes any difference to the way I feel about you?'

His eyes darkened, but he turned away, and walked steadily towards the bathroom. 'Give me five minutes,' he told her softly, 'then I'll show you the rest of the house.'

on to long carved serving tables and sideboards where silver candelabra indicated intimate dinners by candlelight.

'We shan't be lunching in here,' Jake added, noting Rachel's awed expression, and she looked relieved. 'There's a small parlour which we use for family occasions.'

'Thank goodness!' Rachel smiled at him in mutual understanding, and then wondered if he was aware what his direct appraisal could do to her. She decided that he probably was. After all, as he had said, he was no boy, and he must have long appreciated his sexual attraction for women.

As well as the dining room there was Mr Courtenay's study, an impressive book-lined room, where Jake confessed he had suffered many a dressing down, and a smaller, less imposing sitting room, with a rack of paperbacks and a colour television.

'Television!' Jake muttered, grimacing. 'I've watched more television in the last three months than I've ever watched before.'

Rachel regarded him sympathetically. 'Will you tell me what it was like—the breakdown, I mean? I'd like to know.'

'Why?' His dark eyebrows quirked. 'So you'll recognise the symptoms if it happens again?'

'No!' Rachel was indignant until she saw him smile and realised he was only teasing her. 'I just want to share everything with you, that's all.'

'We'll talk about it,' he promised softly, and then it was time to join his parents for lunch.

A young woman was waiting with the Courtenays in the drawing room. Tall, and quite slim, with curly dark hair and conventionally attractive features, she was apparently quite at home here, and although Rachel had a moment's uncertainty, Jake's friendly exclamation of 'Sheila!' confirmed that this was his father's secretary, Dora Pendlebury's daughter.

Jake and Sheila shook hands, and she inquired warmly after his health, while Rachel accepted the glass of sherry

the women here to find someone to console me.' His eyes narrowed as they lingered on Rachel's bent head. 'Unfortunately, Sheila didn't fit the bill.'

'Right,' said his father, with some relief. 'Now we've got that out of the way, perhaps we can get on with our lunch.'

Rachel picked up her fork as Mrs Courtenay said defensively: 'It's as well to make these things open!' and chancing a look at Jake was warmed by the intimate smile he gave her. It had been quite a visit, but she was learning.

After lunch they all adjourned to the drawing room again, and seated on the couch beside Jake, with his arm along the cushions behind her, discussing in general terms their plans for the future, Rachel thought she had never felt more content. It was only as the shadows began invading the corners of the room, and Jake suggested it was time they started back, that a little of her earlier uncertainty returned to torment her.

Jake was leaving the hotel at the end of the week. That was one of the things which had been decided, and he would make all the arrangements for their wedding at Hardy Lonsdale parish church in two weeks' time. After the wedding, they would spend Christmas with his parents, as Jake had said, and return to London in the New Year. There was no talk of a honeymoon, but Rachel knew that marrying Jake was the important thing, and where they spent their life afterwards didn't matter, so long as they were together. Even so, she dreaded seeing Della again, and telling her their plans. There were times when she was torn by the terrifying certainty that she was dreaming all this, and only Della's cruel insinuations were real.

It was dark by the time they got back to the hotel, and Jake was looking distinctly strained. It had been his most strenuous day since the start of his illness, and he asked Rachel if she would mind if he went straight to bed.

Standing with him in the gloomy interior of the underground garage, Rachel was concerned by the greyness of his features. 'Would you like me to come with you?' she asked, and then realised at once what she had said when

cream from her dressing table, but now she slammed it down on to the glass surface again with unnecessary force, her lips moving angrily. 'Well, hear this, Rachel! Don't you come running to me when things start going wrong and expect me to take you back again, because I won't!'

'Oh, Della——'

'Don't "oh, Della" me! I've been good to you, and this is how you repay me!'

Rachel let her go on, wishing there was some way she could have avoided this. If only Della had tried to understand, instead of pretending a martyred outrage over a relationship she had tried to establish for herself.

'Where are you going?'

As Rachel reached for the door handle, the older woman's shrill tones made her turn back. 'I'm going to my room, Della,' she replied carefully. 'There's no point in continuing this. We both know that you don't really feel anything but contempt for me, and last night you were quite prepared to dismiss me out of hand.'

'I should never have gone through with that,' exclaimed Della indignantly. 'Everyone says things they don't mean in moments of stress. I was upset and angry. How else did you expect me to react?'

Rachel heaved a sigh, and determinedly opened the door. 'I'm tired, Della,' she said, tension causing a tight band around her temples. 'I don't want any dinner, but I'll take Minstrel out later on, don't worry.'

Della sniffed, dabbing at her nose with the back of her hand. 'I wonder what your mother would think about you marrying a man more than twenty years your senior,' she demanded.

'I imagine that so long as I was happy, she would be happy, too,' retorted Rachel shortly, and slammed the door behind her.

In her own room, she flung herself on the bed with a feeling of intense restlessness. If only there was someone she could talk to, she thought dejectedly. Some woman

playing the heavy. We had a good time together, but Jake and I . . .' She made a helpless gesture. 'I'm sorry.'

Carl was encouraged by her changing attitude. 'I only wanted you to know that I shall miss you,' he explained, making a concerted effort to win her approval. 'I mean . . .' He possessed himself of one of her hands. 'We were just getting to know one another.'

She was still looking at him abstractedly when the lift doors opened and Jake emerged, and immediately Rachel was conscious of her hand held within Carl's and of how their appearance must seem to an onlooker.

She pulled her hand away from Carl's as Jake strolled across to join them, his expression revealing none of the jealous anger she had nervously expected to see. Carl visibly came to attention as his employer approached, and his polite: 'Good morning!' was at once a greeting and, to Rachel's ears, an unspoken plea for understanding.

'Good morning.' Jake returned the salutation easily, smiling at Rachel and bringing a becoming sparkle to her eyes. He looked much better this morning, she thought with relief, the lines of strain carved the day before ironed out after a night's rest. 'I'm sorry I couldn't join you for breakfast,' he added. 'I overslept.'

'I—er—I understand you and Miss Lesley are going to get married, sir,' Carl faltered awkwardly. 'Congratulations!'

There was a moment's silence after his words while Jake toyed with the buttons of his leather overcoat and the other sounds of the hotel went on, effectively creating a barrier around them. Rachel felt herself tensing, and her eyes darted anxiously to Jake's.

At last he said: 'Thank you. But I'm sure you don't call my fiancée Miss Lesley any more than I do.'

Carl was taken aback. 'Well, I——'

'Relax.' Jake's tone was laconic. 'I don't expect you to stand on ceremony, Carl. Besides, you've been out with her yourself, haven't you?'

'Just to a disco,' Carl protested, and Jake nodded.

'So what?' Rachel frowned. 'Why are you telling me this? Why should I want to know about the resale value of a diamond ring?'

Jake shrugged. 'I just thought you might be interested. Denise sold all her jewellery when she inherited the Perrucci emeralds. I believe she made somewhere in the region of twenty-five thousand pounds!'

Rachel understood now. 'You mean you're only buying me this ring so that I'll have something of value to sell when we split up, is that it?' she demanded.

'You've got the picture,' he agreed tonelessly, and her heart thumped sickeningly in her ears.

'Well, if that's all you're buying it for, forget it!' she declared, controlling the treacherous tremor in her voice. 'Whatever you care to believe, I don't want your money, and you can keep your diamond rings for someone who'll appreciate them!'

Jake stared down at her broodingly. 'Brave words,' he drawled. 'What it is to be young and have ideals!'

Rachel heaved a deep breath. 'We're quarrelling, and there's no need for it,' she exclaimed. 'Just because you came downstairs and found Carl holding my hand——'

'Not just because of that!' he corrected her grimly. 'I've done a lot of thinking since yesterday, and I'm becoming more and more convinced this was a crazy idea!'

'What!' Rachel's knees went weak.

'You heard what I said, Rachel. I have one disastrous marriage behind me. Why should I assume ours would be in any way different, particularly as there are other complications.'

'What other complications?' she cried, turning up her coat collar against the chill wind blowing off the sea, and he regarded her half impatiently.

'Us,' he said flatly. 'You and me. The material differences between us notwithstanding.'

'I see.' Rachel wondered if she had ever felt so wretched. She couldn't imagine so, not even when her parents died. 'So—you want to call it off?'

grasped his hand. 'Let's go down on the beach. I'm shaking so much people will think I've got pneumonia!'

'Then we'll go and buy a ring,' he said firmly, ignoring her instinctive recoil. 'Because I want to put my mark of possession upon you, that's all.'

cousins. They were people Rachel had been introduced to before the ceremony, but she couldn't remember any of their names now.

'Rachel!' Mrs Courtenay turned at her approach, and smiled warmly. Since the marriage had become a definite possibility, she had done her utmost to make amends for her earlier behaviour, and although Rachel still regarded her with a certain amount of caution, she had to admit that Jake's mother had been very kind to her. It was because of her that Rachel was now wearing this model gown, purchased by Mrs Courtenay through her connections with the London fashion houses, and in spite of Rachel's protest that she had enough clothes, one or two other items had found their way into her wardrobe.

'Such a beautiful dress,' sighed Mrs King admiringly, as she joined them. 'You're a lucky girl, Rachel.'

'Yes.'

Rachel's husky affirmative was less than enthusiastic, and Della gave her a curious look. 'Are you planning to stay here until after Christmas?' she inquired. 'Aren't you having a honeymoon?'

Rachel sighed. 'Jake still hasn't to overdo things,' she explained, and his mother hastened to add that she and Mr Courtenay were leaving that evening to spend a few days with her sister in Dorchester.

'Naturally, we don't want to intrude,' she added archly, 'although the west wing is quite apart from our rooms at the other side of the house. Still, I always think a newly married couple need a little time alone together, don't you?'

'Stop embarrassing the girl, Sarah,' exclaimed her sister, earning her new niece's undying gratitude for her intervention. 'Jake and Rachel have all their lives ahead of them. There's time enough to be alone.'

'You're just like Charles, Lydia,' exclaimed Mrs Courtenay impatiently. 'You both behave as if you've never been young yourselves.'

Jake's Aunt Lydia merely gave a wry smile and turned to

at the realisation that he was her husband now. 'I—no.' She gestured towards her still half-full glass. 'Is everything all right?'

'You tell me,' he answered gravely. 'I saw you with Yates. What was he saying to you?'

She gave a breathy little laugh. 'Are you jealous?'

'Yes.'

His reply was as unexpected as it was off-hand, spoken in a throw-away tone that in no way drew attention to the importance of its meaning. Rachel gazed up at him wide-eyed, and her lips parted in confusion.

'Carl was just—admiring my dress,' she got out jerkily. 'Jake, you have no need to be jealous of him!'

His eyes moved meaningfully over the vee-necked bodice of her gown, lingering on the shadowy cleft between her breasts, just visible above the fine lace. 'Was that all he said?' he demanded, not acknowledging her protest, and she sighed.

'Yes. At least—well, he said you were a lucky swine, but that's a matter of opinion, isn't it?' she joked, and then getting no obvious response: 'How—much longer will this affair be going on?'

Jake's hand slid down her arm to her wrist, his fingers stroking her palm before interlacing themselves with hers. 'I thought I heard Denise's name mentioned,' he drawled quietly, his lips brushing close to her ear, as Carl's had done, but with infinitely more effect on Rachel. 'I hope you're not going to start lying to me this early in our relationship.'

Rachel turned to him aghast, but what she had been about to say was swallowed up by Mr Courtenay's booming voice, exclaiming loudly: 'Give someone else a chance, Jake! Can't you wait until you get her alone before you start monopolising the girl?'

Jake's father had obviously been imbibing too freely in the vintage champagne, and his face was unnaturally flushed and blotchy. Beads of perspiration stood out on his

'I'm not trying to.' For once Della seemed sincere. 'But—well, whether you like it or not, I am the nearest thing to a mother you're likely to find today, and perhaps we should —talk about things.'

'I know the facts of life, Della.'

'I'm sure you do.' Della glanced round casually to make sure their conversation was not being overheard, and then went on: 'But between theories and their practical counterparts there's an enormous gulf.'

'Della, please——'

'No. Listen to me: I know what I'm talking about. I've been married, remember. I know what it's like.'

Rachel sighed, and looked round hopefully for Jake; but he and his father were standing by the buffet tables, apparently deep in conversation, and short of walking off and leaving her, she was obliged to listen to what the older woman had to say.

'Of course,' Della mused, 'marrying an older man makes it a little better for you. I mean, Jake has had experience, hasn't he? But—be warned. It's not the romantic event you imagine it to be.'

'Has that been your experience, Mrs Faulkner-Stewart?'

Unobserved, Jake had returned, and was now standing behind Rachel, listening to their conversation with a distinct lack of self-consciousness. But Della's plump face turned crimson.

'Why, Mr Courtenay,' she exclaimed, pressing a hand to her breast. 'I didn't see you there.' She cleared her throat. 'I—er—I was just trying to explain to Rachel that—that women don't necessarily feel about these things as a man does.'

'What things?' Jake was evidently enjoying himself, and the hand he slid around Rachel's waist, drawing her back against him, was definitely possessive.

Della could not have looked more embarrassed. 'I know you're only teasing me, Mr Courtenay,' she exclaimed, striving to sound coquettish. 'Tell me, what does it feel like being married again?'

'Are you married, doctor?' she asked tautly.

'Indeed I am.'

Rachel glanced round. 'Is your wife here with you?'

'I'm afraid not.' Then, in answer to her unspoken question, he added: 'My wife is in a nursing home at present, recovering from the birth of our third daughter just a week ago.'

'Oh!' Rachel gulped, 'So you have three daughters.'

'And a son,' agreed Maxwell Francis, nodding. 'He's the eldest, fortunately, or I've no doubt his life wouldn't be worth living with three sisters!'

Rachel relaxed a little. 'Please—give my best wishes to your wife and tell her I hope to meet her in person one day.'

'I'll certainly do that,' he said, with evident pleasure. 'You and Jake will have to come and visit us when you get back to London. We live just outside, actually, but Jake knows the way.'

'I'd like that.'

'So long as you don't mind a gang of children and a mad dog crawling all over you, you'll enjoy it,' put in Jake humorously, and Maxwell laughed again.

'Yes, that's the way of it,' he admitted.

'I shan't mind at all,' Rachel asserted. 'I like children.'

'Good,' Maxwell grinned. 'Then the next time I see you, I shall expect to hear there's a little Courtenay on the way.'

Rachel was taken aback by his frankness, but again Jake came to the rescue. 'Not quite yet, Max,' he assured him firmly. 'I want my wife to myself for a while.'

A couple whom Rachel recognised as being business associates of Jake's came to join them just then, and conversation became less personal. John Masterson, as the man was called, was able to satisfy some of Jake's queries about his business affairs and while the two men were talking together, Mrs Masterson asked her how soon they expected to get back to London.

'Not until the New Year,' inserted Maxwell Francis, with some definition. 'Jake knows how I feel about it, and I

looked particularly dark against the pristine whiteness of the shirt, the gold chain around his neck visible as he unfastened the top two buttons.

Rachel stepped delicately across the floor towards him, and he studied her appearance through heavy-lidded eyes.

'Well?' he said evenly. 'That's that. The party's over.'

'Is it?' Rachel drew a deep breath. 'I thought everything went very well, didn't you?'

'Very well,' he conceded dryly. 'You carried it off beautifully. Everyone thinks I'm a very fortunate man.'

'Do you think that, too?' she ventured daringly, but he moved away towards the stairs, mounting them two at a time to reach the landing.

He stood looking down at her for a moment, and then he said abruptly: 'I need a shower,' and turned towards his rooms in the west wing.

Rachel waited a few minutes to see if he would come back, but when he didn't, she too mounted the stairs, standing uncertainly on the landing, wondering whether she was expected to find her own way to his apartments.

On impulse, she walked into the drawing room again, empty now that the caterers had cleared away the remains of the buffet, but still full of the scent of Havana tobacco; and from there into the small parlour where Dora had laid an intimate supper for two. How the housekeeper must have disliked doing this, Rachel thought with perception, recalling Dora's animosity towards herself. But if Jake had wanted to marry Sheila, he could have done so years ago, and they shouldn't blame her because he did not find the older girl attractive.

The table looked quite romantic. The napkins were red, and matched the centrepiece of glowing poinsettia, that spread its scarlet leaves in a bowl of dark green fern. There were fragile stemmed glasses, and glittering silverware, and two scented candles to light for illumination. Another bottle of champagne nestled in a bucket of crushed ice beside the table, and Rachel touched its frosted neck with hands that were not quite steady.

look at him warily. 'I—it's beautiful,' she said politely, and he pulled a wry face.

'This is my mother's idea of a honeymoon suite,' he remarked mockingly. 'The bathroom's through there, and you'll see that she's had all your belongings transferred to the wardrobes here.'

Rachel licked her dry lips. 'I—I see.'

'I'll leave you to change,' he continued, straightening from the indolent slouch he had adopted, and a few moments later the outer doors closed behind him.

The bathroom was just as luxurious, with gold-plated taps, and a creamy-yellow sunken tub. Wall mirrors were embarrassing, frankly reflecting her slender body from all angles, and she was glad when the steam misted them over and hid her blushes.

Back in the bedroom again, Rachel opened the doors of a tall wardrobe and surveyed the contents hanging there. Her clothes, brought from the hotel, fitted into less than half its width, but the new garments Mrs Courtenay had bought her helped to fill the empty space. Among them was a filmy green chiffon, and it was this that Rachel took out and laid reverently on the bed.

Her make-up took little time, although she gave some attention to her eyes, stroking mascara on to her lashes, and a luminous green shadow to her lids. Then she slipped the filmy gown over her head and allowed its sinuous folds to settle lovingly about the slender curves of her body. Surveying her reflection in the long mirrors of the wardrobe, she had to admit that she had never worn anything that gave her such a sensuous appeal.

Trembling a little, she turned from the mirror and ran unsteady fingers over her hair. She was ready, and in spite of the confidence the gown had given her, she was still nervous. The things Della had said kept coming back to torment her, and Jake's own attitude of detachment did not help matters.

Leaving the bedroom, she crossed the lounge and emerged into the corridor. Although the whole of the build-

advised, filling her glass, and she permitted herself a half-suppressed sigh of frustration before tasting the wine.

It was delicious, and she swallowed what was in her glass quite quickly in an effort to give herself more confidence. Jake, who had taken his seat, leant across to refill her glass, and it crossed her mind that if she was not careful, she would overdo it. She wasn't used to alcohol in any form, and she had eaten little enough today to absorb an abundance of fluid.

The meal was a simple one: a cold consommé was followed by sliced meats with salad, and the gateau to finish was oozing with cream. Throughout the meal, Rachel drank as little as possible, although it was difficult to get anything down her parched throat without liquid. However, the soup went down quite freely, and the gateau displaced her discomfort at not doing justice to the salad.

Jake spoke little as they ate, and Rachel's efforts to introduce a lighter note into the proceedings all went unacknowledged. But at last it was over, and Jake brought to the table the jug of coffee which had been keeping hot over a small burner.

'A liqueur, I think, would not come amiss,' he remarked, uncorking another bottle, but Rachel looked up at him apologetically.

'Not for me, thank you,' she refused, forcing a smile to her lips. 'Are you trying to get me drunk?'

Jake's eyes narrowed. 'That would be a futile exercise, wouldn't it?' he challenged, and she was forced to look away.

'I just thought——'

'I'd like you to try this liqueur,' he persisted. 'Won't you? For me?'

It was the nearest he had got to saying anything personal to her all evening, and Rachel drew a trembling breath. 'Well—all right,' she conceded unwillingly. 'But—just a little.'

'Of course.'

The glasses they used were thimble-size, and Rachel re-

her eyes and she steeled herself for the seemingly endless stretch of floor that divided her from remembered couches where she might lay her aching head. Her wedding day, she thought with some self-pity! And she had almost ruined it. Or was that Jake? She tried to think coherently. What was it he had said earlier, before that wall of indifference had descended between them?

'Do you need some help?'

Jake's cool voice seemed to come from a great distance, and she was shocked to find him standing right beside her.

'No,' she declared vehemently. 'I'm all right. I can manage.'

'Are you sure?'

Was that concern in his tones? Did he actually reveal a little anxiety now? Rachel blinked and stared at him defensively. 'I've told you. I'm all right. That—that liqueur—it —I didn't like it.'

'I'm sorry.'

He was polite, but the dryness was back in his voice and she wished she could think of some politely sarcastic retort which would wipe that cool detachment from his face.

She couldn't. It was no use. Her brain was muzzy along with the rest of her faculties, and clenching her fists, she started across the floor. But the floor was behaving in a most unusual way, too, dipping and weaving so that the pattern on the carpet swam into a haze of green and gold that made her eyes ache with weariness. Oh, to close her eyes, she thought longingly, and wondered at the hard hands that reached for her before unconsciousness claimed her . . .

violated her unresisting lack of consciousness.

Bathed and dressed, she had gone in search of her husband, only to discover he was not in the house, and only Dora was about, clearing their dishes from the night before, and tidying the living rooms. She had given the girl a frosty greeting, and although she offered breakfast Rachel had refused everything but coffee.

When Jake eventually came in from the stables, he had found his new wife curled up on a sofa in the drawing room feeling very much alone and abandoned. And his first words had not been reassuring to her: 'Did you sleep well?'

At this, Rachel had swung her legs to the floor and got to her feet. She had been eager not to let the night's events determine their future relationship.

'I'm afraid I must have passed out,' she said apologetically. 'I'm sorry.'

'You were tired,' he corrected her, moving to the hearth where Dora had re-lit the fire.

In close-fitting denim pants and a grey knitted shirt he was disruptively attractive, and she wanted to go to him and put her arms about him and show him how much she loved him. Two days before she would not have hesitated, but somehow something had changed, and now she found herself wondering what he would have done if she had followed her instincts.

'Jake,' she had said instead, unconsciously appealing. 'Jake . . . can we talk?'

'Are we not?' he countered, and she felt the same sense of defeat she had felt the night before. But she would not let him get away with it.

'Jake . . . since yesterday afternoon——'

'After the wedding?'

'Yes.' She paused. 'Jake, has something happened? Is something wrong? Why are you treating me this way?'

Her outburst at least had the effect of bringing a little more colour to his unnaturally sallow cheeks. But his eyes remained bleak as he surveyed her. 'I tried to tell you how it would be,' he spoke at last, slowly. 'You knew it wasn't

'I do care about you, Rachel,' he declared stiffly, and then meeting her tormented gaze, he turned away to kick savagely at the logs in the grate. 'I do,' he repeated harshly. 'But there is no middle way, Rachel. That's why we have to try and make one. If I were to go on as before, there would be no turning back. Knowing you were my wife, do you think I could let you go?'

'I don't want you to let me go,' she breathed, welcoming the glimmer of emotion that overran his words, but when he turned to her again, he had himself in control once more.

'A few weeks,' he said firmly. 'If we're going to spend the rest of our lives together, a few weeks won't make that much difference.'

Rachel's shoulders sagged. 'So you really were trying to get me drunk last night.'

Jake sighed. 'You were overwrought, Rachel. I had to do something. Could you think of a better way?'

Rachel shook her head helplessly. 'A deliberate plan,' she said bitterly. 'And I thought I'd let you down.'

Jake stifled an oath. 'We have so much to learn about one another——'

'I'm beginning to believe it.'

'—but if there's to be no trust between us . . .'

Rachel drew a deep breath. 'So what you're really saying is that we should live as—individuals—for the next few weeks.'

'Friends, I hope.'

'Friends?' She turned away, feeling completely shattered. 'And—and when your parents come back? What then? Won't they think it strange that you—that we don't share the same bedroom?'

'Not necessarily. I've been ill, as my mother is so fond of pointing out. If it becomes general knowledge, I shall tell her that as I don't rest very easily, I sleep alone to avoid disturbing you.'

'You have it all worked out, don't you?' she exclaimed tremulously, sick with the realisation that he was adamant

she ate for the sole purpose of avoiding painful comment. Jake noticed, of course, and remarked upon her fining features in private, but with him she was scarcely civil anyway, and in his father's house there was little he could do.

Jake spent a lot of his time at the stables, but although Rachel was attracted to the horses, she maintained an indifference in an effort to gain some reaction from him. She didn't have a lot of experience with men, however, and her unsophisticated attempts to arouse his antagonism and through it his emotions bore little fruit.

On one occasion, bored by her own company and having refused Mrs Courtenay's invitation to join her on a shopping expedition and knowing Jake was working with the horses, she had put on her coat and left the house. It was a cold, frosty afternoon, only a few days before Christmas, and her intention was to ask Jake if he would drive her into Glastonbury. She had some foolish idea of buying him a present with a slice of the unused allowance he was paying her, and maybe reaching him in that way. But before she had even reached the stables, she had heard Sheila's husky laughter and guessed that her husband was not alone. The temptation to turn back there and then was strong, but anger had driven her forward and in through the open stable door.

As she had expected, Sheila was there, her tall slim figure attractively clad in matching pants and jacket of lovat tweed, a red scarf slotted at the open neck complementing the darkness of her hair. She was leaning over the stall where Jake was grooming one of the horses, helping him up from a squatting position, and he, too, looked easy and relaxed. That they were both surprised to see Rachel was obvious, and Rachel did not stop to think before rushing into reckless accusation.

'Oh, I'm sorry,' she exclaimed with heavy sarcasm, 'am I intruding? I thought you were busy, Jake, but obviously that only applies so far as I'm concerned!'

'Rachel!'

Jake stared at her angrily for several seconds, and then he said savagely: 'Don't you ever do that to me again!'

Rachel separated her chattering teeth with her tongue. 'And—and if I choose to do so?' she returned jerkily. 'How will you stop me? I don't understand why—why you didn't marry her! At least with her you wouldn't need time to get to know one another. You seem—you seem to know one another very well as—as it is!'

Jake regarded her grimly for a few more terrifying moments, and then with a violent ejaculation he reached for her, jerking her into his arms with a roughness that made her lose her balance and fall helplessly against him. His lips imprisoned her startled mouth, his teeth grinding against hers until her lips parted wilfully, allowing him full possession of the moist sweetness within. One hand was beneath her hair at her nape, while the other slid the length of her spine, moulding her body against his with increasing intimacy.

'All right,' he muttered, releasing her lips to turn his mouth against the soft curve of her throat, 'if you persist in baiting me . . .'

His mouth covered hers again, but this time his hand went behind her legs, swinging her feet off the ground so that he could carry her into the bedroom and put her down on the silken bedspread. Uncaring of his boots, or that he had come straight from the stables, he flung himself beside her, and the weight of his body was an intoxicating accompaniment to the stirring urgency of her senses.

Whether he would have gone the whole way and taken her in anger, she was never to know. No sooner had his fingers unfastened the buttons of her shirt exposing the rose-tipped fullness of her breasts to his caressing touch, than someone started knocking at the outer door of the suite and Dora's voice could be heard calling that Jake was wanted on the telephone.

There was a moment when she thought he was going to ignore the housekeeper's summons, when his tongue stroked the hardening nipples, and her heart leapt with a

It was exactly the kind of humiliation needed to crack Rachel's failing efforts at composure, and she had left the table at once, her handkerchief pressed tightly to her lips. She had half expected Jake to follow her—half expected his parents might suggest he should do so—but she had been mistaken. She had spent a lonely evening in her room and an even lonelier night . . .

Christmas Day had proved to be slightly less fraught. Dora had been given the day off, Mrs Courtenay assuring her that she and Rachel could handle the already-prepared turkey, and when gifts were exchanged at the breakfast table, Rachel had been warmed by Jake's parents' presentation of a silver cross and chain. They told her it had been given to Jake when he was christened by his grandmother, Mr Courtenay's mother, and had been in the Courtenay family for generations. Her own gifts to them were much less valuable—a lace shawl for Mrs Courtenay, and a new pipe for Jake's father, but they seemed delighted.

She had not expected a gift from Jake, particularly not in the circumstances, but she had counted without his desire to maintain the illusion of their marriage for his parents' sake. His gift to her was a matching set of earrings and necklace, delicately cut sapphires and rubies adorning slender gold chains, that swung from her ears when she moved her head, or rested with fragile fire against her warm skin. She didn't know what to say when she lifted the lid of the jeweller's box, or how to thank him with his parents watching her every move.

'They're beautiful!' she murmured inadequately, meeting his gaze with uncertain eyes, only too aware of the gulf that was stretching between them. 'Thank you.'

Jake inclined his head casually, apparently intent on examining the diamond-studded cufflinks his mother had given him, but Mr Courtenay was not to be deprived of a more demonstrative approach.

'Give him a kiss, girl!' he exclaimed jovially, puffing away at his new pipe, and Rachel felt obliged to get up out of her chair and approach her husband. She half expected

was in finding ways to fill her time. It wasn't enough for Jake to say that she had the use of a car or an allowance that might comfortably have fed a family of four. She wanted to be part of his life, not just an onlooker on the sidelines. How else were they to get to know one another?

Jake usually managed to get home in time to shower and change for dinner at around seven-thirty. This was the high spot of Rachel's day, although invariably after the meal was over he took himself off to his study for a couple of hours, only emerging when she was thinking of going to bed. She guessed he was trying to show her how difficult it was being the wife of a man like him, but if he was prepared to spend his nights with her, she would suffer the days gladly.

Now Rachel looked at her watch. It was almost seven, and she had been sitting staring unseeingly at her reflection in her vanity unit for the past half hour. Jake should have been home by now, but she had not heard him come in, and as his bedroom was adjacent to hers, she could usually detect some sounds when he was changing or taking his shower. She herself had showered some time ago, and lying on the bed was another of the dresses Mrs Courtenay had chosen, a primrose-yellow silk jersey, with a high roll collar and hip-flaring skirt. To think, she thought wryly, only a couple of months ago she had seen Della in this position, and now ... She had never envied the older woman, but although she would not change her life now, she envied the girl she used to be.

A door slammed somewhere, and she started nervously. Jake must be home. She licked her dry lips and picked up her mascara brush to finish darkening the golden tips of her lashes. It wouldn't take her more than a minute to put on her dress and Jake would need at least half an hour to bathe and change. Her pulses quickened as they always did when she thought of him, and she felt an impatience with herself. She was a married woman now, not a schoolgirl on her first date. She must learn to control her foolish emotions.

think?' She drew an unsteady breath. 'Is that what you *really* think?'

'What do you mean?'

'I think there's more to being a wife than attending parties with one's husband,' she declared tremulously. 'And my tastes lie in another direction entirely.'

Jake pulled his tie free and unfastened the top buttons of his shirt. 'So,' he said, not looking at her, 'will you come?'

Rachel made a resigned gesture. 'If you want me to.'

'Good.' Jake turned back towards the door. 'It's informal. We'll leave in about an hour.'

Rachel spent at least half that time taking another look at her limited wardrobe. The yellow jersey was all right for an evening at home, but what ought she to wear to an informal dinner party? She tried to remember what Della used to wear on informal occasions, but her tastes had been so much more sophisticated than Rachel's own.

She eventually decided to wear trousers, the black velvet pants and waistcoat she had worn the night Carl took her to the discotheque. That it was also the night when Jake had asked her to marry him she put to the back of her mind, refusing to associate her desire to wear the suit with any faint hopes she might have of arousing Jake's awareness.

When he saw her, however, his eyes did flicker for a second, and then he said quietly: 'Wait—I have something for you.'

He left the living room for a moment, and when he returned he was carrying a soft fur coat over his arm. Rachel viewed the sable skins without enthusiasm, but she turned obediently at his approach so that he could drop the warm garment about her slim shoulders.

'Thank you,' she said stiffly, realising her midi coat would not have stood examination by the kind of friends he had, and his eyes narrowed questioningly.

'Is something wrong?' he queried. 'Don't you like the coat?'

'It's very nice,' she replied politely. 'Shall we go? Or

121

oblique one. Sure of his love, she felt she could have faced anything, whereas who knows, there might be women at this party who knew her husband better than she did.

Jake locked the car and took her arm to lead her towards the house. He must have felt her trembling because he looked down at her quickly, and said: 'Don't be nervous. They won't eat you.'

'Won't they?' Rachel felt she was answering all his comments with a question. 'Did these people—well, were they friends of—of Denise's, too?'

Jake's mouth turned down at the corners. 'They knew Denise, yes. She was very—sociable.'

'Were you?' Rachel asked, as they mounted the shallow steps to the porch, and a wry smile touched his lips.

'Not in the way you mean,' he told her dryly, and she was unaccountably reassured.

One ring at the bell brought a black-clad maid to let them in, and within seconds it seemed to Rachel they were surrounded by people. People of all ages, young and old, dressed in formal and informal attire, so that Rachel's velvet suit went unremarked, much to her relief.

Their host and hostess pushed their way through the throng to be introduced to Jake's new wife, and Jon Forrest was unquestionably charming. His wife, Petra, was slightly less friendly, and Rachel guessed she had been a friend of Denise's, and therefore felt a certain amount of loyalty towards Jake's first wife.

But she was introduced to so many people during the course of the next hour that faces began to run together, and names simply refused to stay put. Jake did his best to stay with her, but so many of the women wanted to talk to her about her background, about how she and Jake had met, and when they decided to get married that inevitably they were separated.

The Forrests, it appeared, had no children, and the ground floor of their house had been thrown into one enormous room, but even so, guests still seemed to find it necessary to sit on the open-tread stairs. There was a bar,

know what a bitch Denise was. Maybe he decided not to make the same mistakes again.'

'Ah, but have you heard? Princess Denise is a widow, no less! Old Vittorio couldn't stand the pace, apparently. Anyway, she's on the loose again, and what's the betting she'll make a beeline for London?'

'To see Jake, you mean?'

'Who else? You know she never really cared about anyone else. Jake refused to be at her beck and call every minute of the day and night, and she decided to teach him a lesson, I guess. It didn't work out quite the way she expected.'

'His breakdown?'

'Well, she must have had something to do with it, mustn't she? After she left, Jake buried himself in his work, and look what happened!'

Rachel's throat felt dry. She wished with all her heart that she had made her presence known before this convesation began. Now she was obliged to go on listening to things she would so much rather not have heard.

'And she's a widow now, you say?'

'Yes.' The other girl lowered her voice slightly. 'I did wonder whether that might not be why Jake got himself married so precipitately. I mean, he must know Denise will want to see him again, and how galling it will be for her to find that he's married now.'

'I see what you mean.'

There were a few moments' silence when Rachel thought with bated breath that she had been discovered. But then two other doors opened and closed, and with fumbling ineptitude she let herself out of her self-imposed prison.

She stood for a few moments in the kitchen before going in to join the party again, oblivious of the activity of the hired staff going on around her, trying to recover some sense of reality. But the things she had overheard were still ringing in her head, and alongside them came the thought that perhaps they were right. Perhaps Jake had married her to thwart any thoughts his first wife might have of taking

On unwilling feet she made her way back to the noisy crowd thronging the living rooms of the house, and the first person she encountered as she stepped through the door was her husband. Jake's face was taut with anger, and he caught her arm roughly when he saw her, wrenching her towards him. At any other time she would have welcomed the contact, but right now she was too disturbed.

'Where the devil have you been?' he demanded, his whisky-scented breath fanning her cheeks, dark eyes narrowed between long sooty lashes. 'I've been looking for you for over half an hour!'

Rachel's head swung back dazedly, her hair gold-tipped strands of bright relief against the sombre velvet of her waistcoat. 'I—I went to the toilet,' she answered automatically, and then, as the shock of his appearance began to fade, she added stiffly: 'How much longer are we staying?'

His grip on her arm eased slightly. 'Aren't you enjoying yourself?'

Rachel straightened her spine. 'Not particularly. Are you?'

His lips curled. 'I thought you might have welcomed the opportunity to sample a taste of the high life. Jon and Petra's parties are usually very popular.'

Rachel shrugged her slim shoulders, looking down pointedly at his hand on her arm, and with a similar gesture he let her go, pushing his hands deep into the pockets of his trousers. He glanced over his shoulder at the exuberant crowd behind them, and then drew his dark brows together.

'Do you want to go home?'

Rachel sighed, realising her unwillingness to join in the festivities could be construed in several ways. Did she want Jake to think that she couldn't handle it? In spite of what she had learned she wanted to please him, whatever his

well, I'm just not used to—to gatherings of this kind.'

'Nor am I, believe it or not,' he retorted grimly, and she noticed a faint slurring of his speech. 'All right. Let's get out of here.'

The Forrests seemed genuinely sorry that they were leaving. 'You must come again soon, when there aren't so many people,' Jon exclaimed gaily, patting Jake's shoulder. 'But I don't blame you, taking yor wife away while you still can. You're a lucky man.'

Jake's smile was polite. 'I know. And thanks again.'

It was a frosty evening, and Rachel breathed deeply of the fresh night air. It was so good to be out of the smoky atmosphere in the house, and away from the all-pervading noise of human voices raised above the music from the record-player.

But the sudden chill had a different effect on Jake. He lurched slightly as they made their way towards where he had left the Lamborghini, and with a sense of dismay she realised the unaccustomed amount of alcohol he had consumed had reacted on him. He swore angrily when he could not get his key into the lock of the passenger side door, and with a determination she had scarcely known she possessed, she took the keys from him and opened the door herself.

'You'd better get in,' she said firmly. 'I'll drive—if you'll direct me.'

Jake stared at her with difficulty through the shadowy light cast from the house. 'Are you sure I am capable of doing that?' he inquired with sarcasm, but she ignored him and walked round to open the other door.

With a sound of self-disgust, he subsided into the passenger seat, and Rachel levered herself behind the wheel, adjusting the safety harness with hands that were not quite steady.

'I'm sorry,' he said quietly, as she endeavoured to make herself familiar with the controls. 'This has never happened to me before. I guess I thought I could take it. I used to be able to.'

She glanced up to find him loosening his coat, and his eyes flickered impatiently away from hers. 'I'm going to bed,' he said abruptly. 'If you want anything else, ring for Mrs Madigan.'

Rachel held the magazine open in her hands, looking at him over the pages. 'She'll be in bed, won't she?' she exclaimed. 'I shouldn't dream of disturbing her at this time of night.' She paused, faint colour entering her cheeks once more. 'Is there anything you need?'

Jake shook his head, and turned away, walking towards the door which led to the hall which in turn gave access to the bedrooms. 'I'll say goodnight, then,' he added briefly, and left the room.

When he had gone, Rachel threw the magazine she was holding down on the table again, and stared impotently towards the door which Jake had just closed behind him. He had gone to bed, just like that, without even waiting for her to go to her own room.

She thrust her hands angrily into her pockets, and as she did so her fingers encountered the soft fur of the sable coat. It was a beautiful coat, she thought reluctantly, running her fingers up over the lapels. So smooth and silky; it had a sensuous appeal. She looked again at the closed door, and then, as if coming to a decision, she walked swiftly towards it.

Her bedroom had white walls, a fluffy white carpet, and a white bedspread; shades of cold virginity, she thought now, with sudden insight. The only relief came in the curtains which were threaded with strands of blue and lilac, and hung from floor to ceiling. The adjoining bathroom continued the design, with tiny blue and lilac roses patterned on the tiles which until now Rachel had found quite charming. But tonight she was disturbed and restless, and time had become her enemy, not her friend, making her fight against the core of practical good sense inside her that told her to forget what she was thinking, and like the ostrich, bury her anxieties.

Turning on the shower, she stripped off all her clothes,

which mothers had been warning their daughters about for years? She was married, it was true, but she didn't feel married, and married people didn't behave as she and Jake were behaving. She had given little actual thought to the culmination of her plans, and now her eyes opened wide in half-fearful anticipation. What if she found she couldn't go through with it? What if she froze up on him as she had heard could sometimes happen? How humiliating that would be!

Dejectedly, she turned back to face the room again. What was the use? she thought glumly. She was simply not up to it. She was not sufficiently sure of herself—or him— to play the role of seductress.

So intent was she on her own condemnation that she paid little attention to the first knocking at her door when it came. It was not until it happened a second time, accompanied by Jake's imperative: 'Rachel!' that she realised what was happening.

Spinning round on her heels, she hurried to the door and opened it, holding the soft furs closely about her. Jake was leaning against the wall outside. Only once before had she seen him without his clothes, and that was on the first occasion she had visited the Priory, when she had gone with him to his rooms while he changed. But tonight he was not wearing a bathrobe, just white silk pyjama trousers, that hung low on his hips and outlined the dark skin beneath. He must have taken a shower, too, because his head was damp, and tiny drops of moisture curled the fine hair covering his chest down to his navel. She could see the hard bones of his rib-cage, and the flatness of his stomach, and her senses tingled expectantly.

Jake surveyed her broodingly for a few moments, and she was sure he had not missed the fact of her bare legs below the sable coat. Then he said curtly: 'I'm sorry to disturb you, but do you have any aspirin? I've got a lousy headache now, and Mrs Madigan doesn't appear to have provided anything like that.'

'Oh!' Rachel realised she had been holding her breath

probing her upper lip. 'Jake—don't go!'

She stretched out a hand to grasp his arm, but the hard muscle she touched was taut and unyielding. She looked up at him desperately, willing him to show some compassion, but the gentleness in his expression had dissolved as swiftly as it had appeared. Her spirits reached their lowest ebb when his free hand came to release her clinging fingers.

'Rachel.' His tone was half tolerant, but he shook his head. 'Rachel, be sensible.'

'I don't want to be sensible,' she protested huskily, moving closer to him, and felt the involuntary shudder that passed through him. 'Jake—love me!'

Jake looked wearily towards the ceiling. 'Rachel, let me go. You'll regret this as much as I will in the morning.'

'No, I won't.' She pressed even closer, and stepping back he, came up against the door jamb behind him so that the muscles of his legs were tangible even through the thickness of her coat.

The warm scent of her body rose into his nostrils to mingle with the musky scent of his own, and he looked down at her with eyes that revealed the torment he was fighting. 'What are you wearing under this?' he demanded harshly, and almost of their own volition, his hands parted the skins to reveal the rose-tinted flesh beneath.

He stared down at her silently for several seconds, his breath coming more quickly, and then, with an oath, he gathered her yielding body close against him, his hands sliding naturally beneath the weight of the sables.

'Is this what you really want?' he asked thickly, burying his face in the curve of her neck, and she allowed the coat to fall unheeded to the floor as she wound her slim arms around his neck.

'Really, really,' she breathed, and he propelled her inside the door again and slammed it closed with his foot.

It was ecstasy feeling the closeness of their bodies, and when his hands slid down to her hips, pressing her intimately against him, she trembled with a hunger she hardly understood.

A curious lethargy enveloped her at the realisation of his nearness, and she stretched sinuously, arching her body as the emotions he had evoked the night before returned to torment her.

Her movements disturbed Jake, and in the half light that filtered through the curtains she saw his eyelids flicker, and the dark lashes sweep upward.

'Rachel?' he murmured, half questioningly, and she nodded and wriggled closer to him.

'I'm sorry,' she confessed softly. 'I woke you,' and his eyes narrowed as with returning consciousness he became aware of her slender form beside his beneath the silk covers.

'I slept here?' he probed, then, half to himself: 'Of course I did. I remember.' He rolled on to his back, putting both hands to the back of his neck. 'God, I remember!' He turned back on to his side and stared at her anxiously: 'I hurt you. I'm the one who should be sorry.'

'Don't be.' She was eager to reassure him. 'I—I—it was my fault. I asked you to stay. I wanted you to. Please—don't be angry.'

'Angry? God!' His hand touched her almost as if he couldn't prevent himself, sliding up over the fullness of her breast to close around the hollow of her throat. 'I'm not angry—not with you anyway. But this is what happens when a man can't hold his liquor!' he derided himself harshly.

Rachel felt as if he had slapped her. 'I—I see,' she got out chokingly. 'That—that was all it was, was it?'

His mouth hardened. 'Do you think I'd have hurt you otherwise? There are gentler ways of going about it. My God, I must have behaved like an animal!'

Rachel licked her dry lips. 'It doesn't matter——'

'But it does!' He spoke fiercely. 'It should never have happened. But even looking at you now, I could——' He broke off savagely. 'You must have one hell of an opinion of me.'

'It's over . . .'

to her again, and this time she had been as eager as he, prepared to bear anything to stay in his arms. But what had begun with apprehension had turned to perception, and then she had been lost in the demands of her own senses. She had scaled the heights with him, shared the tender aftermath, and learned what loving was all about.

Feeling the sensuous brush of the silk sheets against her breasts, she realised she was naked in the bed, and suppressing the smile which seemed determined to tilt the corners of her mouth, she swung her feet to the floor. What time was it? And where was Jake? Had he left for his office? Had he left her any message? How would she exist through the day until she could be with him again?

It was later than she thought, after ten o'clock, and she went quickly into the bathroom to take a shower. Her toes encountered something hard on the carpet, and bending, she picked up the bottle of aspirin tablets she had given Jake the night before. Her cheeks dimpled. He had not taken any after all...

She was drying herself with a fluffy green bathsheet when there was a knock at her door. Her senses quickening, she called: 'Come in!' and smothered a grimace when Mrs Madigan appeared.

'Good morning, Mrs Courtenay,' she greeted the girl politely, and Rachel couldn't altogether stifle the automatic response she felt towards the name. 'I'm going to the shops now. Is there anything I can get you?'

Rachel pulled the shower cap from her head, and draped the towel sarong-wise under her arms. 'I don't think so, Mrs Madigan, thank you.' She paused. 'Has—did Mr Courtenay leave for the office as usual?'

'He was late,' replied the older woman conversationally. 'Did you enjoy the party, madam?'

'The party?' Rachel looked bewildered for a moment, and then gathered her wits. Of course, Mrs Madigan no doubt thought they had been late back from their visit to the Forrests. 'Oh, well—it was a change,' she concluded at last. Then: 'I'm afraid I'm not much used to parties.'

She guessed he glanced at his watch, and then he said: 'In about an hour, hmm? Twelve o'clock. At Pasticcio's—it's an Italian restaurant off Regent Street. Get a taxi. The driver will know it.'

'All right.' She was breathless. 'I'll be there.'

'Good.'

She knew he was about to ring off, and said foolishly: 'Jake?'

She heard his sigh. 'Yes?'

'Jake—thank you.'

'For what?' He sounded half impatient.

She paused, unable to put into words over a telephone what she really meant. 'Why—for asking me to lunch, of course,' she answered softly, and he uttered a mild oath before ringing off.

set her down in Regent Street, only a few yards from its entrance. She paid the driver too much in her haste to get inside, and good-humouredly he handed her a pound back.

'It wasn't worth it, miss,' he told her with a grin. 'But thanks anyway.'

Rachel's lips twitched, and stuffing the extra pound note back into her bag, she hurried towards the restaurant. What if Jake wasn't there? she thought anxiously. What would she do? Go to his office? She knew where the skyscraper block was where his companies occupied several floors, but she had never been invited there.

A black-coated waiter opened the door at her approach and smiled benignly. 'Good morning, madame,' he greeted her politely, and she managed a faint smile before searching the discreetly-lit room beyond for a familiar face.

'I—er—I'm looking for Mr Courtenay . . .' she was beginning nervously, when a tall figure emerged from the shadows. 'Oh, Jake!' she breathed in relief, and he made brief introductions to Antonio, the head waiter, before escorting her to the alcove where a table for two was laid.

'I'm sorry I'm late,' she exclaimed, in a subdued voice, after the waiter had taken her coat, but Jake just indicated that she should sit down on the low banquette and after she had done so joined her, his thigh firm and masculine against hers.

'A drink, sir?'

The waiter was hovering, and Jake glanced sideways at Rachel before deciding. 'Two gin and tonics,' he ordered after a moment, and the waiter bowed and went politely away.

'I . . . I couldn't get a taxi . . .' Rachel started to continue her explanations as soon as they were alone, but Jake's mouth silenced her, reminding her of the passionate intimacy they had shared.

'You're here now,' he said when he lifted his head, apparently oblivious of anyone but her, and her limbs melted beneath the warmth of his gaze.

plained the situation, I thought of that. But it's no good. It wouldn't work. I need all my concentration to get through this deal, and it'll be bloody hard as it is, fighting the jet lag, without the distraction of knowing that you're waiting in the hotel for me.'

Rachel's momentary thrill of possession disappeared beneath a wave of depression. 'But how long will you be away?' she protested.

Jake lifted his shoulders wearily. 'A week—ten days at most. It's the Pearman deal that I was handling before I became ill.'

Rachel pressed her lips together. 'But isn't there anyone else who could go?' she cried. 'Surely after—after what happened, you ought to be delegating some of your work.'

Jake rubbed the side of his nose. 'Yes. Well, that thought had occurred to me, too, and once this deal is through, I'm considering shifting some of the burden on to Petrie's shoulders.'

'Petrie?' Rachel frowned.

'Yes. Gordon Petrie. You haven't met him yet, have you? He's a good man. He's practically kept the place going while I've been away. He and my father both.'

'Your father?'

'Oh, yes. It was his company in the beginning, you know.'

'And he reported to you?'

Rachel sounded disapproving, remembering the occasion she had seen the elder Mr Courtenay at the hotel, and Jake smiled. 'No,' he said firmly. 'You should know better than that. But I'm not denying that once I went to stay at the Priory, he was keen enough to hand over the responsibility again.'

Rachel looked at him anxiously. 'But you know what Mr Francis said!'

'Max? He's an old woman. And you're beginning to sound like my mother!'

Rachel drew back, hurt by his apparent insensitivity, and with an exclamation, he grasped both her hands in his, and

145

Italian recipe that dates back quite a number of years.'

Rachel shook her head. 'You choose. Like I told you, I'm not very hungry.'

Jake regarded her with warm concern. 'Stop thinking about tomorrow and think about today,' he urged. 'A week will soon pass. Then I promise you, it will be some time before I agree to go away again.'

Rachel sighed. 'All right,' she yielded. 'I know I have to get used to this, but . . .'

'I know. It's too soon after——' He broke off. 'It might interest you to know that this life I lead wasn't my choice at all.'

'No. Your father told me. You would have preferred to work with animals, wouldn't you?'

'Mmm,' Jake nodded. 'If I thought——' He broke off again, but this time Rachel urged him to go on: 'Well . . .' He hesitated. 'If I thought Petrie could handle it, I'd be tempted to buy a place out in the country, like Max for example, and keep a few animals of our own.' He smiled. 'And only come into the city two—maybe three days in the week.'

Rachel clasped her hands together. 'That would be marvellous!'

He looked surprised. 'You'd like that?'

'I'd love it.'

He frowned. 'But wouldn't you rather live in London? I mean . . .' He shook his head, 'I know some women would.'

'You mean—Denise,' she ventured daringly. 'I'm not like Denise, Jake.'

He gave a wry grimace. 'You don't have to tell me that.'

'Besides,' Rachel caught her lower lip between her teeth, 'if—if we have children, the country is a so much nicer place for them to play.'

Jake turned towards her, his smile definitely provocative, but then the waiter arrived to take their order and by the time he had gone, the moment's intimacy had passed.

All the same, Rachel wished she had taken the opportunity to tell him what she had overheard at the Forrests'

'I will. You do the same. And phone Mother if you have any problems.'

'She knows you're going away?'

'Yes. I spoke to Father yesterday morning, as soon as I knew.'

Rachel nodded. 'What did he say?'

Jake grinned. 'Told me I was a fool for leaving you behind.'

'You are!' she declared, just for a moment allowing her real feelings to show.

Jake bent towards her. 'You'll be all right, won't you?'

'Who? Me?' Rachel controlled herself again, and feigned a nonchalance she was far from knowing. 'Of course.'

'Of course.'

A look of bitterness distorted his expression for a moment, and cold fingers touched her heart. 'Don't say it like that!' she cried, and the look disappeared as swiftly as it had come.

'I was just thinking what a fool I was, too,' he told her swiftly, but she had the distinct feeling he had not been thinking that at all.

His mouth sought hers, and their lips clung together for a moment in time. Then, without another word, he set her free, turning away and striding towards passport control without a backward glance.

Rachel didn't wait to see the huge jet take off. Unable to withstand the surging emotions inside her, she hurried down the stairs and out to where Madigan was waiting for her, climbing into the back of the chauffeur-driven Daimler Jake used on these occasions without saying a word.

Back at the apartment, it was worse, with Jake's personality imprinted on every article she touched. It made her wish she had a mother, someone she could go home to and share her misery with. She even thought of Della without bitterness and the others at the hotel, and she felt a curious longing to go back there among people who knew and possibly cared about her.

She could always go to the Priory, of course, but Sheila Pendlebury was there, and while the older girl had neither

149

'You'll come?' Mrs Courtenay seized on her weakening immediately. 'Oh, good! Shall we say Thursday—or Friday?'

'I was thinking perhaps—Saturday morning,' conceded Rachel defeatedly, thinking with some relief that it was only a matter of forty-eight hours after all. But Jake's mother's terms were rather different.

'Very well,' she agreed without argument, 'and perhaps Charles and I could run you back on Monday and spend a couple of days at the apartment,' making Rachel's return to London merely an extension of her visit.

'Well, actually,' she began recklessly, without stopping to consider the possible consequences of what she was about to say, 'if I do come down to Hardy Lonsdale, I might go on to Torquay afterwards and spend a couple of days at the hotel, with Della.'

'With Della?' Mrs Courtenay sounded disapproving. 'But I thought—that is, Jake told us that you and she—well, were not exactly soulmates!'

'We're not,' replied Rachel levelly. 'But she was a friend of my mother's, and I think she'd like to know that I'm well and happy.'

In actual fact, she didn't know any such thing, but the idea of having Mrs Courtenay at the apartment until Jake came home didn't bear thinking about. She didn't think she could stand any more unsubtle innuendoes about Denise at this time, and nor did she want Sheila coming to their home on the pretext of seeing Mr Courtenay, leaving traces of her personality in the atmosphere.

'Well, you must do what you want, of course,' Jake's mother was saying now, 'but I shouldn't make any hasty decisions about going to the Tor Court. You may find you'd prefer to stay at the Priory, after all. So . . .' She paused. 'When is Jake due back?'

'A week tomorrow,' responded Rachel tautly. 'Or sooner if he can manage it.'

'Oh, I shouldn't expect him any sooner, my dear,' Mrs Courtenay declared firmly, with the air of one who knows.

voice sounding far too clear to really be coming all those thousands of miles. 'The time here is around seven-thirty, and everyone's just about to have dinner.'

'Dinner!' Rachel was incredulous. 'But you must be exhausted! How was the flight?'

'Boring,' he responded laconically. 'Hours and hours of unadulterated boredom. I managed to sleep for a while, but like you say, I am pretty tired now.'

'Oh, Jake!' It was stupid, but she couldn't think of anything else to say, and the precious seconds were ticking away. 'I'm so glad you phoned.'

'Are you?' he paused. 'What have you been doing?'

She felt an hysterical sob rising in her throat. 'Nothing,' she declared chokily. 'Nothing—but watch television. Oh, and your mother phoned. She wants me to go down there for the weekend.'

There was a moment's silence before he asked: 'Will you go?'

Rachel sighed. 'Probably.'

'You don't have to, you know.'

'I know. But——' she moved her shoulders defeatedly, realising how impossible it was not to understand how he must feel, 'I think they'd like me to go.'

'I'm sure they would.' Jake sounded convinced of that. Another silence, then: 'Did I wake you?'

'No.' The sob escaped in a nervous laugh. 'I couldn't sleep.'

'Take a drink,' he advised softly, and her lips trembled helplessly.

'J-Jake!'

'Yes.'

'Hurry home!'

'I don't need you to tell me that,' he answered roughly. 'Right now, I feel like getting on the next plane back to England.'

'When—when do you go to San Francisco?'

'I fly up tomorrow morning. I have a meeting with the Pearman board at two o'clock. I'll try and ring you lunch-

CHAPTER ELEVEN

RACHEL drove herself down to Hardy Lonsdale on Saturday morning. Jake had said she might use the Lamborghini, but with Madigan's permission she was driving the Daimler, which seemed a more conventional kind of vehicle. It was three days since Jake's departure, and he had contacted her every evening, reducing the miles between them through the medium of the telephone. She had still not got over the thrill of hearing his voice, and half resented the realisation that this evening she might not be alone to receive his call. He had promised to ring her at the Priory for the next two evenings, but she had not yet mentioned that she might go on to Torquay on Monday, refusing to admit to a certain reluctance in doing so. Carl Yates would be at the hotel, and she didn't want Jake to jump to the wrong conclusions. All the same, unless she changed her mind about Jake's parents accompanying her back to London, she was bound to stay at least one night at the Tor Court.

It was lunch time when she arrived at the Priory, and Mrs Courtenay must have been looking for the car, because both Jake's parents came out to greet her as she parked on the forecourt.

'Darling Rachel!' Mrs Courtenay embraced her warmly, and then Mr Courtenay was shaking her hand, leaning forward to bestow a light kiss on her cheek.

'Did you have a good journey?' he asked, taking her case, and Rachel nodded, telling them that the roads had been quiet, as they walked indoors.

'And how are you?' her mother-in-law wanted to know, as they climbed the stairs to the first floor. 'Have you been very lonely?'

Rachel sighed. 'A little,' she conceded reluctantly. 'But yesterday I went to the Francises' house, and met Max's wife, Jean, and I enjoyed that.'

In truth, she had not wanted to accept the consultant's

just wanted to let us know that he hopes to be home by Wednesday.'

Rachel put down her handbag, and sank down on to one of the couches. 'That was—thoughtful of him,' she murmured, but she couldn't help wishing he had rung his parents first.

Sheila joined them as they were having a drink before the meal. She came into the room with her usual assurance, and gave Rachel a confident smile. 'Hello again,' she greeted the younger girl cheerfully. 'How are you?'

'I'm fine, thank you.' Rachel forced a smile. 'Are you?'

'Oh, yes, I'm very well.' Sheila's embracing manner was almost patronising. 'How is Jake?'

'Finding the trip a strain, I think,' Rachel told her quietly. 'It's so soon after . . .'

Her voice trailed away, and Sheila's lips curled. 'After getting married, do you mean?'

'No!' Rachel was indignant. 'I mean after his illness, of course.'

'I've no doubt it's a combination of both,' remarked Mrs Courtenay with her usual lack of tact, and Jake's father pulled a wry face at her.

'Oh, come on, Sarah! Jake's no weakling! It's going into that office every day that's getting him down. As a matter of fact, he was talking about that last night. Seems he's had this idea of shifting some of the responsibility for Courtenays on to Petrie's shoulders, and only going into the office every other day.'

'But could he do that?' exclaimed his wife, and Rachel too found she was waiting expectantly for Mr Courtenay's answer.

'I guess he could,' Jake's father said at length. 'It's only conceit that makes us think we're indispensable. Besides,' he looked gently at his daughter-in-law, 'I believe he wants to buy a place outside of town, where he can raise a family. Isn't that right, Rachel?'

Rachel's mouth tilted upward. 'I think so,' she admitted shyly, but not even Mrs Courtenay's delighted reception of

a weekly periodical explaining methods of breeding and rearing animals. Rachel frowned.

'Are they Jake's?'

Sheila nodded, and continued flicking through them. 'Mr Courtenay wants me to find an article he remembers seeing in one of them.'

'What about?'

Sheila looked up at her then, her eyes insolently appraising. 'Does it matter? You don't know anything about horses, do you?'

Rachel bit back the retort that sprang to her lips. Instead, she said evenly: 'I'm sure Jake wouldn't mind if you took the magazines along to your own room. There's no need for you to look at them here.'

Sheila's gaze didn't waver. 'Why should I? I like it here.' Rachel had no immediate answer to that, and the other girl went on: 'What's the matter, Rachel? Surely you're not jealous of me just sitting here in Jake's old room while you're making no objections to the company he keeps.'

'I'm not jealous!' declared Rachel, but even to her ears it didn't sound entirely convincing. And then, as the rest of what Sheila had said registered: 'What are you implying? Why should I object to the company Jake keeps?'

'Why indeed?'

Sheila shrugged annoyingly, and resumed flicking through the pages. Rachel could feel her nails digging into the palms of her hands and she told herself severely to calm down. The girl was being deliberately provocative, encouraging her to ask questions, the answers to which might well be ambiguous. Obviously Sheila was not immune from jealousy herself, and as Rachel had expected this she should be prepared for it.

Turning away, she was about to close the door again when Sheila spoke again. 'I should ask Jake how long Denise plans to stay in San Francisco,' she remarked casually. 'Or maybe she's flying back to England with him!'

'Denise!' Rachel couldn't deny the involuntary exclamation, but she felt furious when she saw Sheila's triumphant

159

Jake's call. As it was, she was obliged to go with Jake's mother and assume a cheerfulness she was far from feeling, knowing that sooner or later she had to face the fact that maybe Jake had lied to her.

Tea seemed to take an interminable time, particularly as Rachel was not hungry, and couldn't even be tempted by the delicate wafered sandwiches Dora had provided. Mrs Courtenay noticed her abstinence, of course, and drew her own conclusions, but Rachel wished it was only Jake's absence which was making her feel so desperate.

Eventually she reached the seclusion of her own suite and kicking off her shoes, curled her toes luxuriously in the soft pile of the carpet. Perhaps she was jumping to conclusions herself. Just because Denise was in San Francisco did not mean that Jake had gone there to meet her. He might not even know she was there. Like London, San Francisco was a big place, and Jake had business matters to occupy his time. Or did he?

Disgusted by the trend of her thoughts, she walked through the bedroom into the bathroom, and turned on the taps. She would take a bath, relax in the warm water, and let its soothing fragrance dispel the unpleasantness Sheila had been so willing to create.

She dressed for dinner with extra care, determined not to let Sheila see how her malicious gossip had affected her, and was rather disappointed to find only Mr and Mrs Courtenay waiting for her in the drawing room. When she casually asked if they were dining alone, Jake's mother replied that Frank Evans, the veterinary surgeon, had been invited to join them, providing Mr Courtenay agreed not to spend the whole evening talking shop.

'All I seem to hear these days is horses, horses, horses,' she declared impatiently, and her husband gave Rachel a knowing grin before asking what she would like to drink.

'That's a pretty dress,' he commented, as Rachel moved to join him, and she looked down at the amber-coloured silk with thoughtful eyes.

'Your wife chose it for me,' she conceded, trying to be-

161

Mr Courtenay showed her into the study, and then went out again, closing the door as she picked up the receiver.

'Hello, Jake!'

'Rachel! So you arrived safely?'

'Yes, I'm here.' She paused. 'How are you?'

'Bearing up.' Was it her imagination, or did he sound restrained somehow? 'How about you?'

'Oh, I'm fine.'

'The parents looking after you?'

'Yes. As per your instructions.' She couldn't resist that small jibe, but before he could take offence at it, she went on hastily: 'How's business?'

'So-so.' There was a moment's silence, and now she felt sure she was not mistaken that Jake had something else on his mind. 'By the way...'

'Yes?'

'I shan't be able to phone you tomorrow. Ralph Pearman's invited me out to his place for the day, being Sunday and all, and I can hardly ask to make a transatlantic phone call from there, can I?'

Rachel's legs gave way and she sank down weakly into the squashy leather chair behind the desk. 'Who—who is Ralph Pearman?' she asked faintly, giving herself time to recover.

Jake sounded surprised. 'You know! I mentioned him the other evening. He's handling the deal here for the organisation.'

'Oh, yes.' Rachel felt slightly sick. 'That Ralph Pearman.'

'Rachel?' He sounded concerned now. 'Rachel, are you all right? Have you been drinking? You sound—sort of—slurred somehow.'

'No, no, I'm fine.' Rachel cleared her throat. 'So you'll phone me Monday? But not here. At—at the hotel.'

'The Tor Court?' His voice was noticeably cooler now. 'Yes, Mother told me what you'd suggested.' He hesitated. 'I'd really rather you went straight back to town.'

Rachel's knuckles hardened. 'Would you?' She straightened her spine. 'Why?' A pause. 'Don't you trust me?'

her, asked, 'What did she want? Why did you have lunch with her?'

Jake sighed again. 'She's a widow now, did you know that?'

'Did you?'

'Of course.' He sounded impatient. 'Vittorio died six weeks ago.'

Rachel digested this with difficulty. So Jake had known soon after their marriage that his wife was a widow—soon enough to have this marriage annulled if he had wanted it. If only he had told her!

'Anyway,' Jake was going on, 'they spent a lot of time in the States when Vittorio was alive, and they have this house out at Carmel which Denise now wants to sell. She heard I was in town, and asked if I'd lunch with her and give her some advice about her affairs. That's it!'

Rachel breathed more easily. 'I see.'

'And now I'd like to know who started all this,' he muttered grimly. 'Who was it? Mother? Father? I can't think of anyone else who knew who might have spoken to you.'

'It doesn't matter——' Rachel was beginning urgently, when the study door suddenly opened and Mrs Courtenay put her head round.

'I hope I'm not interrupting,' she whispered pointedly, 'but you have had quite a while to yourselves. Do you think I could speak to Jake for a minute?'

Rachel stared at her mother-in-law frustratedly. What could she say? How could she explain that Mrs Courtenay could not have chosen a worse moment to interrupt them?

'I—Jake——' she spoke into the phone. 'Your mother wants to speak to you.'

'Rachel, wait——'

But Mrs Courtenay needed no second bidding, and was already taking the phone from her daughter-in-law's reluctant hand. Rachel herself hovered in the background, wondering whether she would get another opportunity to speak to Jake, but then, aware of his mother's half-impatient stare, she felt obliged to leave the room.

Courtenay in the morning, and then, after an early lunch, Mr Courtenay took them for a drive down to the coast. It was still cold, but the sun was shining as it had the previous day, and Rachel's spirits rose a little. Jake would be home in three days, and soon this past week would be just a rather uneasy memory.

'Are you going down to Torquay tomorrow?' asked Mrs Courtenay that evening, as they sat by the fire after dinner, and Rachel glanced at her doubtfully.

'I—well, no, I don't think so,' she conceded, and Mr Courtenay looked up from the chess pieces he was studying.

'You're going straight back to town?' he asked, and she nodded.

'I wish you'd told us sooner,' exclaimed Jake's mother regretfully. 'I mean, you heard me arrange to help the vicar's wife with Tuesday's jumble sale this morning.'

'What has that to do with anything?' asked her husband, and Mrs Courtenay sighed.

'I told Rachel that we might go up to town with her for a few days,' she told him impatiently, but Mr Courtenay just looked annoyed.

'You did what!' he declared grimly. 'Us—go up to town with Rachel! Don't be ridiculous, woman. I can't go up to London this week. You know I've got Harrison coming to have a look at the mare, and Sam wants me to go to Risford market with him. Besides,' he glanced understandingly at Rachel, 'do you want the lass to think we don't trust her? Good lord, you've brought her down here, don't you think that's enough?'

Mrs Courtenay pursed her lips. 'I might know horses would come before your own daughter-in-law!' she retorted, and again Rachel interposed herself between them.

'Really,' she exclaimed, 'he—that is, Jake's father is right. I'd really rather have a few days alone before Jake gets back. I—have things to do. I want to do some shopping first of all.' Some new clothes, she thought with en-

'Well, it was no secret,' pointed out her husband mildly. 'Jake told me the day before he left that she was staying in California.' He looked at Rachel. 'He wanted to tell you, but he was afraid you might get upset.'

Rachel managed to maintain a composed countenance, but as usual, Mrs Courtenay had to have the last word. 'I can understand how he felt,' she put in, with disruptive candour. 'I mean, Denise was his wife, after all, and she's a widow now. And we all know Jake divorced her, not the other way around.'

'*Sarah!*' Mr Courtenay's tone was threatening, but his wife didn't seem to hear.

'She was a beautiful girl,' she went on reminiscently. 'They made a very handsome couple, everyone said so. If Jake's breakdown hadn't happened so much later, I'd have said that was the cause.'

Rachel left the Priory at ten o'clock the next morning and arrived back at the apartment soon after one. It was a relief to walk through the empty rooms, re-acquainting herself with her surroundings, knowing she had only herself to please.

Mrs Madigan soon rustled up some lunch for her, and afterwards Rachel rang the Courtenays to let them know she had arrived home safely. Dora answered the call, however, as Mrs Courtenay was visiting the vicarage and Mr Courtenay as usual was down at the stables.

'It's all right,' she assured the housekeeper, when she offered to call Jake's father. 'It's not important. Tell them I'll ring later.'

It was late afternoon when the telephone started ringing, and Rachel hastily put down the book she was reading and went to answer it. She was sure it must be Jake, but when she picked up the receiver, a strange if not entirely unfamiliar voice asked to speak to her.

'This is Rachel Courtenay speaking,' she said, frowning. 'Who's that? Carl? Carl, is that really you?'

A sound from the doorway made her look up and seeing Mrs Madigan she shook her head quickly, putting her hand

freezing hard down here tonight, and after the thaw of the last few days, the roads are pretty slippery.'

'I'll drive carefully,' said Rachel at once. 'And at least the roads aren't busy at this time of year.' She sighed. 'Thanks for ringing, Carl. I'm glad you told me. It's only right that Della should have someone—of her own at the funeral.'

Mrs Madigan looked dismayed when Rachel said she was driving south again. 'But it's five o'clock, Mrs Courtenay!' she exclaimed. 'You can't drive down to Devon tonight.'

'I have to,' said Rachel simply, deciding not to go into unnecessary details about her reasons for going. It was nothing to do with the housekeeper after all, and she would be home again tomorrow evening after the funeral was over.

She filled up the petrol tank at the nearest garage, and joined the M3 going west. She picked up the A30 before reaching Salisbury, and drove on feeling the first real twinges of weariness when she saw how far it still was to Bath and Glastonbury. Her eyes were pricking painfully by the time she reached the next village, and finding it to be Melford she realised with a sense of dismay that she had inadvertently got on to the Warminster road. It meant a detour of some twenty and more miles to get back on to the right road again, unless she turned round now and went back the way she had come.

Turning round seemed the lesser of two evils, but she had to go beyond the village to find a suitable spot. Then, in the darkness, she misjudged the turn, and found her back wheels spinning helplessly over the edge of a ditch.

It was the last straw, and she got out of the car half tearfully, staring at the car's predicament in angry frustration. The removal of her weight from the car, however, was sufficient to set it rolling backwards, and there was an ominous crack as it lurched into the muddy water of the ditch.

'Oh, damn, damn!' she muttered miserably to herself. Now what was she going to do?

At least the village wasn't far away, she consoled herself

171

addressed her from the doorway: 'Will it be all right if I use the phone?'

The girl looked up and then got to her feet. 'You'd be Mrs Courtenay, I suppose,' she said, her plump cheeks radiating a smiling good humour. 'Mum said you were staying the night. Do you want some breakfast? Mum said to get you anything you wanted.'

Rachel smiled in return. 'That's very kind, and I would like some coffee—or tea, if possible. But right now, I'd like to make a call.'

'Of course. Go ahead.' The girl nodded towards the bar. 'There's no one in there right now. Dad's gone into the village to see about your car, and Mum's out back feeding the hens.'

'Thank you.' Rachel paused. 'What's your name?'

'Beth, miss. Elizabeth really. Elizabeth Jopling.'

Rachel nodded. 'Well, I'll make that call now . . .'

Getting through to the hotel took longer than she expected, mainly because she had to search her pockets and handbag for sufficient change to put into the phone box. But eventually the receptionist answered and she asked to speak to Carl.

'I'm afraid he's not here,' the receptionist replied politely, and Rachel stifled an exclamation before saying: 'He must be!' 'No, madam,' the receptionist continued smoothly. 'I'm afraid he's attending a funeral this morning, and won't be back before lunch. Who shall I say has called?'

Rachel slumped against the wall. The funeral was *this morning*, and he had left already! She was never going to make it in time!

'Hello?' The receptionist sounded impatient. 'Hello, are you still there?'

'Yes, I'm still here,' responded Rachel heavily. 'As a matter of fact, I was coming to the funeral myself, but my car's broken down.'

'I see.' The girl sounded a little more understanding now. 'Well, I'm afraid the service is at ten o'clock, so unless you

suggested. 'I mean, I know it's nothing special, but you're welcome to stay if you want to.'

Rachel smiled. 'That's very kind of you, but——'

'I know. You'd rather find an hotel.'

'Not really.' She shook her head. 'I just don't want to put you or your wife to any more inconvenience.'

'It's no trouble,' Mrs Jopling assured her at once. 'The sheets are on the bed now, and one night more or less won't make any difference. Since Beth's two brothers left home, there's only the three of us, and we've plenty of room.'

Rachel didn't see how she could refuse. Besides, she had decided there was no point in going on to Torquay, and it seemed more sensible to stay here until the car was ready than have to return or send Madigan back to pick it up later. But she must get home tomorrow. Jake might be back tomorrow night.

She shivered in anticipation. She would ring Mrs Madigan today and explain the situation so that if Jake rang tonight he would not worry about her.

Mrs Madigan told him she had driven down to Devon, he must have rung the hotel and found out from Carl why she had gone. He was unreasonable! Just because she had not turned up at the Tor Court there was no reason to behave as if she had committed some unforgivable crime. Della was dead! Didn't that mean anything to him? He hadn't liked the woman, she knew, but he must realise that she felt a kind of obligation towards her.

Now she said unsteadily: 'I really don't understand why you're behaving like this. I haven't done anything wrong. I didn't know you were coming home today——'

'Last night, actually,' he put in coldly, but she ignored it.

'——and in any case,' she added, 'I had to come. Carl asked me——'

'He means that much to you?'

Frustration, and the sense of anti-climax she was feeling at having Jake speak to her like this when she had been just longing to be with him again, brought tears of anger to her eyes. 'Oh, Jake, don't be so silly!' she declared, and then the pips sounded, signifying the end of her three minutes. The operator came on the line at once, asking her to put some more coins in the box if she wanted to continue, but Rachel didn't. With a feeling of despair, she replaced the receiver, and then ran swiftly out of the bar before anyone could attempt to sympathise with her.

Her car was ready by eleven o'clock the next morning, and after paying the Joplings more than they asked, she left, eager to get back to London and find out what was going on. It had sleeted a little in the night, and the roads were inclined to be treacherous, so she drove more slowly than usual, chafing at the time she was wasting.

She didn't stop for lunch, and arrived back at the apartment soon after two, to be greeted by an anxious Mrs Madigan.

'Oh, Mrs Courtenay!' she exclaimed with relief. 'There you are! We've all been at sixes and sevens since you left.'

Rachel carried her case into the living room and set it

'Why?' Rachel stared at her.

'It was that call you had that sent you down to Devon, wasn't it?' Rachel nodded, and the housekeeper went on: 'I guessed it was. It was me who told Mr Courtenay that you'd been speaking to someone called—Carl, is that right?'

'Oh, God!' Rachel buried her face in her hands. Slowly she was beginning to understand. She raised her head reluctantly. 'What did he do then?'

'He—he phoned his parents, I think. He told me he'd asked them if you'd said you were going on to Torquay, and his mother had assured him that you'd decided against it.'

'That's true. I had.' Rachel tugged painful fingers through her hair without even noticing it. 'But that was before——' She made a distraught gesture. 'Before—before I married Jake, I worked for my godmother, a Mrs Faulkner-Stewart. She was staying at the hotel in Torquay. She was spending the winter there. Carl—Carl Yates, that is, he's the manager. He rang to tell me that she had a heart attack and died on Saturday. The funeral was yesterday. I—I missed it because I had an accident with the car.'

'Oh, Mrs Courtenay!' Mrs Madigan stared at her in dismay. 'Oh, how dreadful! If only you'd told me!'

'I didn't see any need to,' replied Rachel dully. 'I only intended being away overnight, and Jake wasn't expected back until today.'

'He got back in the early hours of yesterday morning.'

'Yes. So he told me.'

Mrs Madigan put a weary hand to her forehead. 'I don't think he's slept since. When you weren't here, he was frantic.'

'Oh, *God*!' Rachel got unsteadily to her feet and paced anxiously about the room. 'He thought—he probably still thinks I was with Carl!'

'Would you like some coffee, madam?'

Mrs Madigan obviously needed something to do and to please her, Rachel nodded, although food was what she

Mrs Madigan set down the tray again and looked doubt-ful. 'I don't know. He might have been.' She shook her head. 'Why?'

Rachel was loath to tell her, but she had to tell some-body. She held up the empty bottle. 'This contained some kind of drug. It's empty now.'

'Good heavens!' Mrs Madigan stared at her. 'You don't think—you don't think he might have done something—foolish?'

'Something foolish?' Rachel looked blank herself for a moment, before the full import of what the housekeeper was suggesting occurred to her. Then whole new terrifying possibilities occurred to her. 'You don't think——Oh, no! Mrs Madigan, I'm sure you're wrong!'

The housekeeper gave a hopeless shrug of her shoulders, and then she said: 'At first I thought—well, I don't know if I ought to tell you this, Mrs Courtenay . . .'

'Tell me what?' Rachel had no time to stand on cere-mony. 'Oh, go on, Mrs Madigan, do! What did you think?'

'It was that call, Mrs Courtenay. The one this morning. From—from Princess Denise!'

'Denise?' Rachel stared at her aghast, and the other woman hurried on:

'Yes.' She looked uncomfortable. 'Mr Courtenay mumbled something about—about her when he found you had gone. I thought—well, when he went out so early, I thought it might have something to do with her then when she rang I knew it hadn't.'

'Denise is in London?' Rachel was stunned.

'Apparently.'

'But how? When?'

'She flew in yesterday, so she said.' Mrs Madigan sighed, then she said quietly: 'You don't have to worry about her, Mrs Courtenay. Mr Courtenay, he's not interested in *her*! My goodness, when they were married there were some goings-on!'

Rachel was trying to absorb what she had heard, and Mrs Madigan, mistaking her silence, added: 'I know it's not

'Oh, Jake!' She felt weak with reaction. 'Jake, where have you been? I found that empty bottle of pills in the bathroom, and I thought——' She broke off unsteadily. 'I've been so worried!'

'Have you?' He shrugged. 'Now you know what it's like.' Then he made an impatient gesture. 'The bottle contained amphetamines, that's all. You know—stimulants. To keep me awake. Do you have any idea how I felt?'

'But it wasn't my fault, Jake,' she protested. 'I didn't know you were coming back. Carl . . .' She faltered at the look in his eyes. 'Carl rang and—and I just had to try to go to Della's funeral. I told Mrs Madigan I was going to the hotel. I thought that would be enough.'

'But you never got there.'

'No. I . . .' She sighed. 'I tried to turn the car on a narrow road and I ended up in the ditch.'

'So I hear.'

'You hear?'

'Yes.' He straightened, releasing her arms, but she didn't move away from him, just stood there in front of him rubbing the circulation back into her numbed limbs. 'That's one of the places I've been this morning. There—and the Tor Court.'

'You've been to Torquay?'

'Yes. I wanted to know where Yates was yesterday morning when I rang.'

'But how did you know where I was?'

'You forget, you made your call via the operator. I had it traced.'

She gasped. 'I didn't know anyone could do that.'

'They can't. In the normal way.' His lips twisted. 'You've forgotten something else—I do have a little influence in certain areas.'

She shook her head. 'So you spoke to Mr Jopling.'

'Yes. And to Mrs Jopling and their daughter—Beth, isn't it?' Rachel nodded, and he went on: 'They assured me you had spent the last two nights at the Grey Goose.'

His conversation was giving Rachel time to gather her

know. She rang here earlier on this morning. Mrs Madigan told me.'

'Denise!' Jake uttered an expletive that Rachel wouldn't have cared to repeat. 'What in hell does Denise have to do with anything?'

'But—I mean—I thought——' Rachel looked confused. 'I thought that was what you meant.'

Jake half closed his eyes. 'Rachel! Rachel! The whereabouts of my ex-wife are of no more interest to me than the whereabouts of Carl Yates to you! All right, I met her in San Francisco, I told you that. But we meet as—individuals; strangers, almost. My God, we only lived together for about a year of the five years we were married. She would tell you that herself if she was here. If she's ringing me now, it's about that house I told you about. I mean, let's be frank, I do know a little more about finance than she does, and her solicitor happens to be a friend of mine. Does that clear it up?'

'You make it sound so—ordinary,' she exclaimed.

'It is ordinary,' he replied with a sigh. 'Rachel, whatever my mother may have said to you, my infatuation with Denise—and that's all it was—was very brief. It never worked. Denise knows that as well as I do. She probably was happier with her ageing prince than she ever was with me. I never fitted into her world, and she sure as hell never fitted into mine.'

'But you—cared about her . . .'

'I was young and foolish,' he retorted. And then more soberly: 'Perhaps as you are now.'

'Oh, Jake, I'm not foolish. I know what I want.'

Unable to keep away from him any longer, she stepped closer, sliding her arms around his waist and pressing her face against the buttoned fastening on his shirt. For a few moments they remained like that, Jake's body stiff and unyielding against hers, and then his control seemed to snap and with a groan, he gathered her to him. One hard hand turned her face up to his, cupping the fragile hollows of her throat while his mouth played around the edge of hers,

not having that animal tearing up this place.'

Rachel's laugh was soft. 'You mean I can keep him? You don't mind?'

'Well, let's say I'm inclined to be tolerant of anything if it pleases you,' he told her ruefully. Then, more seriously: 'Rachel, this trip has taught me more than a lesson. I think I needed it. It's proved to me that what I feel about you is no fleeting thing, no casual infatuation, like I felt for Denise. I love you. And believe me, I've never said that to any woman and meant it. That's why I've never said it to you before. I wanted to be sure—absolutely sure. And I am now.' He broke off as she reached up to kiss him, and when he spoke again his voice was husky. 'Rachel, be sure you mean it when you say you love me. I don't think I could stand to lose you now.'

'I mean it,' she told him simply, but sincerely, winding her arms about his neck. 'When you were away, I was only half alive. I want to be with you—and care for you—and have your children . . .' She touched his cheek tenderly with her lips. 'And I don't care where we live as long as we're together. I don't think that's infatuation, do you?'

Jake hugged her closer. 'I'm only sorry you had to learn about Denise from my mother,' he muttered half impatiently. 'I wanted to tell you myself before I left, but I chickened out at the last minute.'

'Your father explained about that,' she murmured, hoping Mrs Courtenay would forgive her for not bringing Sheila's name into it right now. There would be time enough for that later. 'But you still haven't told me how you came to be home two days earlier than expected.'

Jake smiled. 'Quite simple really. I turned Sunday into a business meeting instead of a social one. After our conversation on Saturday evening, I just wanted to see you and explain.'

She sighed, pressing her lips to the pulse beating in the hollow of his throat. 'Mmm, I see.' Her tongue appeared provocatively. 'Your heart is pounding, darling, do you know that?'

Did you miss any of these exciting Harlequin Omnibus 3-in-1 volumes?

Anne Hampson #3
Heaven Is High (#1570)
Gold Is the Sunrise (#1595)
There Came a Tyrant (#1622)

Essie Summers #6
The House on Gregor's Brae (#1535)
South Island Stowaway (#1564)
A Touch of Magic (#1702)

Margaret Way #2
Summer Magic (#1571)
Ring of Jade (#1603)
Noonfire (#1687)

Margaret Malcolm #2
Marriage by Agreement (#1635)
The Faithful Rebel (#1664)
Sunshine on the Mountains (#1699)

Eleanor Farnes #2
A Castle in Spain (#1584)
The Valley of the Eagles (#1639)
A Serpent in Eden (#1662)

Kay Thorpe
Curtain Call (#1504)
Sawdust Season (#1583)
Olive Island (#1661)

Great value in reading at $2.25 per volume

Joyce Dingwell #3
Red Ginger Blossom (#1633)
Wife to Sim (#1657)
The Pool of Pink Lilies (#1688)

Hilary Wilde
The Golden Maze (#1624)
The Fire of Life (#1642)
The Impossible Dream (#1685)

Flora Kidd
If Love Be Love (#1640)
The Cave of the White Rose (#1663)
The Taming of Lisa (#1684)

Lucy Gillen #2
Sweet Kate (#1649)
A Time Remembered (#1669)
Dangerous Stranger (#1683)

Gloria Bevan
Beyond the Ranges (#1459)
Vineyard in a Valley (#1608)
The Frost and the Fire (#1682)

Jane Donnelly
The Mill in the Meadow (#1592)
A Stranger Came (#1660)
The Long Shadow (#1681)